6 Demons of Fear

Jody N Holland

ISBN: 1633900312
ISBN-13: 978-1-63390-031-8

DEDICATION

This book is dedicated to the guides that I have had throughout my life. I have been given insight, guidance, and wisdom that have helped me along the way. I am thankful for each of the guides and I pray that I will continue to have incredible guides throughout the rest of my life.

CONTENTS

ACKNOWLEDGEMENTS

I want to acknowledge the creator of all things. My creator has given me the gift of seeing things from a different angle than most and that angle has led to this book. I want to acknowledge you for taking this journey to overcoming the demons of fear that attempt to keep you from the joy and happiness that was always your destiny.

1 WHAT WE FEAR

We fear what is unknown. We fear what we have. We fear what others will think of us. We fear that others will no longer think of us. We fear that we will not matter. We fear that we will be successful and others will take advantage of us. We fear what the past means and what the future holds. We fear too much. These were the thoughts of Jason as he looked out the window and stared at the openness of the rolling hills. Sitting in the café that overlooked the meadow in that small Colorado town, he was searching for exactly why he was being held back from the things that he knew he was supposed to accomplish in life. Jason had spent his life in pursuit of dreams, but continued to find himself falling short of his goals. He would get so close that he could taste victory and then something would happen. He would hesitate. He would walk away. He would back down. It always seemed to happen and he wanted to, no needed to, figure out how to beat this.

He took a sip of his coffee as the gentleman that he had arranged this breakfast meeting with walked up to the table. Jason stood up and introduced himself formally. "My name is Jason Davids." The older gentleman, dressed in jeans and a flannel shirt and tennis shoes, extended his hand and replied, "My name is Joseph Brock, but you can call me Joe." They shook hands and then took their seats. The waitress, having been told that Jason would have another guest soon, was less than 20 seconds behind with a coffee cup in hand and the pot of fresh coffee. "How are you gentlemen doing today? It sure is good to see you this morning Joe." Joe looked up and smiled and responded with, "Good to see you too Lori." Joe was from that area and came to the café at least twice a week. Lori had been a waitress there for the last 5 years, but she told people that she had been there since the dinosaurs roamed the earth. After the coffee was filled and the two indicated that they would not be eating, Jason turned to Joe and began.

"I really appreciate you taking the time to meet with me. I really need someone like you to help me gain some perspective." Joe took a sip of his coffee and nodded at the same time. "Out of curiosity Jason, how did you come to know about me? You aren't from this area." Jason curled up the left side of his mouth in a half smile and looked up and to the left, indicating that he was remembering the path that lead him to Joe. "Well, that is an interesting story." Joe cocked his head to the side ever-so slightly as to indicate that he was interested in hearing the story. Jason continued, "I have started 4 businesses over the last 16 years and have kept getting right to the edge of success and then backing away for some reason. Out of frustration at my last venture where I literally snatched victory out of the jaws of defeat and ended up shutting the whole business down, I decided that I would do whatever I needed to do in order to learn how to be the right person before trying again. So, I began talking to as many successful people as I could, in order to find out about what they knew and what I was missing. I approached Jennifer Stevens in Phoenix about 2 weeks ago. I had heard her speak a year or so earlier at a conference that I went to and had purchased her book. She graciously accepted my request to meet with her, and I flew out to Phoenix. She spent a couple of hours with me and kept referencing 'her sage' as the person that helped her become the success that she is now. I pressed her several times to discover what that meant and she finally told me about you."

Joe calmly continued to sip his coffee, with a wry grin forming on his mouth, waiting for the rest of the story. Jason paused to take a sip of his coffee as well. Then Joe asked, "What did Jen tell you was her key to success.?" "She said it was her ability to beat the demons of fear." Jason shook his head slightly as if to say that he knew that those demons were out there and he just didn't know how to overcome them. "She explained several of the demons of fear to me, but I'm not sure if I totally got what she was saying. I mean, demons?" Jason tilted his head to the side a bit and raised his eyebrows at the same time. At this, Joe broke into a big smile. "They're out there alright. More people give up on their dreams because of those demons than any other reason. They have thwarted the efforts of great men and women and have conned would-be superstars into believing that they were nothing more than common men and women. They have kept people out of office, out of board rooms, and out of the prosperity that was intended for them." Joe continued to get more passionate and more animated as he spoke of the demons. He continued, "It is the demons that haunt before a sales call, before an interview, before a presentation. It is the demons that convince you to do what you know is wrong in order imagine that you are more secure or more liked as a result. These six demons will make every effort to put you in hell on earth if you let them! I know! They did it to me for years. Finally, I had enough and did something about it."

"Wow!" was all Jason could think after the speech that grew in volume, animation, and intensity. He looked at Joe and watched as he calmed himself a little and began sipping his coffee again. Jason thought to himself, "This guy hates those demons." As if Joe could read his mind, he added, "I don't hate them, though. I respect them for what they can do and I never underestimate them. And without a doubt, I never give in to them anymore." Jason finally asked, "When you say demons, do you mean, well, demons?" Jason had a half puzzled, half inquisitive look on his face. "I mean precisely that, Jason. I mean demons. I mean negative thought energy that manifests itself in the ruin of great people and would-be great people alike."

The two just sat and sipped their coffee for a minute. It seemed as if both men needed to let the idea of demons sink in. Jason looked out of the window at the beauty that Colorado had to offer. He was rolling an idea around in his head, of some horned creature trying to keep him from succeeding, and wondered why in the world the devil or a demon would even care what he did with his life. What was so special about him that would make a demon take notice of him?

Joe's thoughts had drifted back to his father teaching him about heaven and hell as a child. He had always believed that there was a God out there. He just didn't understand the balance of power when he was young. At that thought, he turned his attention back to Jason. "Jason, what is the opposite of light?" Jason responded with, "Darkness." "And what is the opposite of up?" Jason chuckled a little at the game that they seemed to be playing now, but responded anyway, "Down." "Hot?" "Cold." "Old?" "Young." Joe continued, "Everything in this world has an opposite. We live in a world of duality. And because of this duality, success cannot exist without failure. Life cannot exist without death. Demons cannot exist without angels." Joe motioned forward with his coffee cup and raised his eyebrows. Jason got the point and began thinking about the dualities that had always existed in his life. The good and the bad things that seemed to balance each other out could be listed on a full ream of paper. They were everywhere. "So, are you saying that it is impossible to succeed unless you fail?" "That is precisely what I am saying, Jason. After all, what do we learn from success?" Jason thought about the question for a minute. "I guess we just learn that we were doing it the right way." "That's true," said Joe. "We learn that what we already knew was right when we succeed. We aren't really learning anything, though. We are simply affirming what we already knew. "Let me ask it this way, Jason… When something doesn't work, what are your possibilities for courses of action?" "Well, I could give up." Joe nodded at him and motioned for him to continue. "I could make a note of the fact that it didn't work like that and then try it a different way." Joe broke into a smile and asked, "And?" "And I could do it again the same way and fail again in the same way." "Very good Jason. The truth is that we have choices in everything that we do. It is the choices that we make that define whether or not our lives will be controlled by the demons. Those choice determine whether we hand over control of our fate to them."

Jason was imagining himself being locked in a prison of self-doubt and giving in to the demons of fear as if they were his jailors. The thought chilled him a little bit because of the number of times that he felt like he was living in a prison that wasn't leaving. He always felt, deep down, that he was holding the keys to the door and could walk out at any time. He just couldn't bring himself to check his pockets and admit to the other inmates that he didn't have to be there. For some twisted reason, he took comfort in knowing that there were lots and lots of other people just like him. "Maybe, even that thought, is one of the demons that Joe is talking about," thought Jason.

"So, Joe, what is it that makes people give in so

easily to these demons and how many people do you think are controlled by them?" "Those are big questions Jason. Let me start with the answer to your second question and one additional item, which may be even bigger. The vast majority of people, I would guess around 97% of people, are controlled by one or more of these demons. Very few people ever break free even though the key to simply walking out of their control is on, or rather in, every living person." Joe gave that a minute to sink in with Jason. He needed him to understand the gravity of the statement that every person had within their control the ability to overcome the demons by simply choosing to do so. "So Jason, tell me what you have seen in other people. Do you see that they are in control or not in control of their fears?"

Jason stared somewhat blankly back at Joe and thought about the question. He knew the answer but didn't want to acknowledge the fact that he was in that 97% of people. He wanted to be in the 3% that controlled themselves through choice. Reluctantly and somewhat slowly, he answered, "I see that most people really don't control the demons of fear. I see that most people go through life simply accepting what the circumstances of life offer, and never taking the risks that would get them to a better place. I see that I am, unfortunately, one of the 97% right now. I don't like the place that I am and I want to change it!" Jason was building up passion as he stated that he wanted to change. "That's good Jason. You have to realize where you are and make the choice to be somewhere else before any change can possibly happen. Now that you know you want to be in a different place in life, we can get started."

Jason breathed a slight sigh of relief at the idea of being able to get started. He knew that Jennifer had said that this was the man who could change his entire world and was the one person that could really make a difference. That was exciting!

"Jason, how much is your freedom from these demons worth to you?" Jason was a little taken back by the question and responded with, "What do you mean, worth?" Even though Jason had always believed that nothing in life was free and that you get what you pay for, he hadn't thought about the idea of paying to get out of his current situation. Joe continued, "People tend to only value the wisdom that they work for and pay for. I know that I can make you successful, however you define that, if you are willing to follow my teachings. I also know that you will only do that if it is painful not to follow them. I have to know how bad you want to be successful, though. As I look at you, I have to wonder if you are looking for an excuse as to why you don't have more money or if you are looking for a way to fix the problem. There are a lot of people in this world that are looking for an excuse."

Jason was both offended and a little ashamed. He knew that deep down he would feel a lot better if he could just justify the reason that he hadn't made it further in life. He wasn't sure that he was ready for the level of work that it would take to make it big. He didn't want to appear cowardly though, especially as they were talking about overcoming the demons of fear. So, he responded with, "I would be willing to pay for the advice." "I think you are missing the point Jason. I want to know how far you are willing to go in order to be successful. I want to know what your freedom from these demons is really worth to you. Let me tell you a little story…

There was a young man that went to a friend of his father's, a multi-millionaire. He told the rich man that he wanted to be like him. The rich man chuckled and asked the young man if he was sure. He then asked the young man what he was willing to give up and how badly he wanted to be successful. The young man quickly responded that he was willing to do whatever it took to be successful. The old man, doubting the sincerity of the young man, asked him to accompany him to the river, just down the hill from his house. The young man gladly accompanied the rich man to the river. Once they arrived at the river, the rich man told the young man to follow him into the river, and he did. Once they were about waist deep in the water, the rich man simply said, "Hold your breath," and then grabbed the young man's head, front and back, and took him under the water. They young man was calm for the first 20 seconds or so and then he started wanting to come up for air. He tapped the rich man's arm to signal that it was time to stop. The rich man just held the young man there, six or so inches under water. Another 20 seconds passed and the young man began to panic. He started struggling against the rich man. He struggled for another 20 seconds or so, until he finally broke free and came up for air. As soon as he rose, he gasped for air and began yelling at the rich man. "What are you doing!? You could have killed me. I almost drown!" The rich man stared calmly at the young man and simply said, "When you want to succeed as much as you wanted air, you will be successful."

The moral of that story was that success had to be all-consuming and the focus on winning had to be more prevalent than the fear of anything. It is the fear that we have that consumes us and takes our focus away from the path that was designed for us. "When you are not wiling to pay for expert advice, it indicates that you don't really believe that you will be successful. It means that you think that you will pay out money, but won't do anything different and won't succeed at a higher level." Jason sat thinking about the story and about what Joe had just accused him of. He was embarrassed because he knew that Joe was right. He knew that he didn't really believe that he would be any different. Deep down, he was trying to justify why he had not succeeded instead of figuring out what to do differently to find success. "Joe, I really do want to figure this out, but you are right. I have been trying to justify my failure instead of overcome it. I think that I have been so scared of failing that I didn't take action at all. I just let the fear consume me. I see now that I am going to fail by not taking action. That is guaranteed. If I take action, I will at least have a shot at succeeding."

Now Joe was smiling. He was looking across the table at his would-be student and was hopeful that he might, just might be able to beat those demons. Jason asked, "So what would you charge me to overcome the demons?" Joe looked as if he was thinking for a moment and then responded, "I would charge you my normal rate of $1,000 per session. Each session will be between an hour and two hours and will be mostly at the café, although we may move to a new location if we need to. We will meet every Saturday morning for the next 7 weeks. That is what it will take to get you past this and into the life that you want." Jason was a little shocked by the price. That was a lot of money for 10 to 20 hours of work. His mind was racing with the thought of where he was, how frustrated he was with that place, and how desperately he wanted "the air" from the story earlier. Joe added, "If you will do exactly as I teach you, you will find success. You can pay me when your success comes. I would estimate that to be 60 to 90 days after our last session." Jason knew that he needed to do this. He looked Joe in the eyes, extended his right hand, and said, "It will be an honor to be coached by you. Let's get started!"

Joe told Jason about a man that he would meet the next Saturday at another café, not far from where they were sitting. Joe said, "John is a unique individual that has the gift of seeing things that most people don't even know exist." They set a time of 7 AM, the next Saturday for the meeting and gathered their things. The first meeting was over and Jason was off to tackle the challenges that he was well aware of in his every day life. He had no idea what the next meeting would hold. There would be no way that he could have imagined what John would reveal to him. He had no idea what a shock it would be to his reality. "And what did Joe mean that John could see things that most people don't realize even exist," thought Jason. The next meeting would change everything.

2 JOHN'S REALITY

John was not like most people. There were a few things about him that made him see the world from a completely different perspective and this set him apart. People wouldn't know that from simply looking at him, but he knew it every day when he would see what was not of this world. He sees things that others only imagine and he has for most of his life. When other people's hair stands on end on the back of their neck, he sees a different reality. He sees why. When people feel a calm that they cannot explain, John sees the reason for the calm. John knows that there is more out there than just what we can see with our physical eyes and he knows how it affects the lives of people all around him. John knows this and wants to help people gain a greater understanding of the other side of reality.

The Story

It started when he was 7 years old. It wasn't a gift that he asked for and he definitely didn't want that gift as a 2nd grader. His gift felt like a curse when he was young. Now, he knows that it is something that he was called to possess. John can see the angels and demons that are all around us. He can see the other reality. He can see the very fabric of the world that makes our world exist and keeps everything in balance. John's reality is that he is a seer.

When John was 7 years old, actually 14 days into being 7 years old, John saw his first angel. The angel presented himself to John when John was sitting in his bedroom, playing with trucks. John could remember looking up and seeing the angel, as clear as a day, and asking, "Who are you?" The angel didn't have some strange Latin name or anything weird. He seemed normal, or mostly normal. He was much brighter than anyone John knew at the time. The angel seemed to radiate light from his body and had a perpetual smile on his face. The angel responded with, "My name is Frank. I am here to help protect you as long as you want me around. Which truck is your favorite?" John remembered thinking that it was natural to have Frank around. And so their friendship began.

He spent a lot of time playing and Frank was a good companion to have. After all, he always wanted to play what John wanted to play. It was almost a year later that John saw the other side of that realm. The other side is what changed his perspective. It was 14 days before John turned 8 that Frank told him that he had been chosen to see things that others could not. Frank told him that there was no reason for him to be afraid of what he saw because God had chosen him as a guide for others.

Immediately after being told that he was a 'chosen guide,' John saw a demon attached to a man walking outside of his window. The demon seemed to notice John as soon as John noticed it. It was hideous. It was hunched over and an ugly reddish black. It seemed to be telling the man how bad his life was and that there was no way that he could overcome the difficulty that he was in. Every time the demon leaned in and dug his claws into the man's soul, the man radiated a light that seemed like pain. The man was tearing himself apart at the beckoning of the demon. It was painful for John to see and he wanted to say something but he was afraid of the demon at the same time. John moved closer to the window and looked intently for another person to walk by. The next person that passed was a lady that was in her late 20's, pushing a stroller. There seemed to be two angels walking with her, looking intently at the two of them and glancing around as if to search for trouble. That was when he spotted it. There was a good-looking figure strolling behind them, or maybe floating, that seemed to be tossing something at the woman's head. The angels were swatting most of them away, but one would get past them every now and then. The woman didn't flinch, so it wasn't a rock. It seemed to be, well, ideas. When one would hit her in the head, she would change colors. The questions that were puzzling John at that young age were, "How did she change colors?

How did the man seem to radiate pain?" This was the beginning of his quest to see the world as it fully is and not simply as it is seen by most people. He wanted to find a way to help people see that there was nothing to be afraid of and that those demons couldn't actually control them. They were just there to try and plant ideas. John knew, even at that age, that ideas can be good or they can be bad. He also knew that people had a choice as to whether or not they accepted an idea as truth. This new reality meant that John's life would never be the same. He often reflected back on that first day of seeing. It was where he had gotten his start and the reason that he was able to help others the way that he did. Despite being required to see the pain of the world, John was grateful that he could help people see the answer to their pain and struggle.

John continued to see more and more of the other reality. He could see what some could only sense and could tell what was going on with most people by what angels or demons were around them, attached to them, and in some cases inside of them. As he sat there at the café, waiting for the man that Joe wanted him to see, he wondered what would come in with this one. John knew that everyone carried one side or the other with them. Each person, by the choices that they made, would attract one side or the other to be a part of their lives. John had his own struggles with the gift, depending on the choices that he was making at the time. His gift, or whatever it was, would go away when he was out of sync with God. When he was aligned with God, his powers of perception seemed to be in tune and working great.

After experiencing what it was like to choose the fear and darkness several times, John was convinced that choosing God was the only choice with a chance of a great outcome. He was often amazed by how often people chose to go in the other direction. His thoughts drifted toward the meeting that was about to happen.

"What would this meeting hold?" That was the overwhelming thought that Jason had. He wasn't sure what this guy was like or what Joe meant by him being able to see things that others can't see. Would he see potential, doubt, intelligence, or what? Jason was a bit nervous as he drove to the new café, close to where he had met Joe the week before. When he did arrive, 12 minutes early, he sat in the car for a couple of minutes, composing himself. He needed to figure out what to do to make his own life more successful and to give something back at the same time. Mostly, he wanted out of the rut that he found himself in. He wanted to live the life that he could see in his mind. He took two deep breaths and turned the ignition off to his car. He grabbed his notebook and pen from the passenger seat and got out of the car. He shut the door, hit the lock button on his remote, and took another deep breath in and out. He wasn't this nervous at last week's meeting. There was just something different about this meeting. He would be exposed for who he really was. He was afraid of that notion for some reason. Deep down he wanted to deal with whatever he needed to deal with, but he just kept having the thought that he should leave before he learned something that he couldn't handle.

"No!" Jason heard himself say the word out loud without really meaning to. John was watching from the window and could tell that this was the person that he was supposed to meet with. This guy's demons were clawing at him and trying to get him back into the car. John looked straight at the demons and said, "Be gone," and just like that, Jason felt good about the meeting. He immediately lost his fear of talking with John. In fact, he was kind of excited about the conversation. He began walking toward the door of the café. Right after he entered, John was there to greet him and said, "You must be Jason." Jason was a little taken back, but figured that Joe had described him well to the new coach. "I am," responded Jason. "And, you must be John," said Jason. "I am indeed," quipped John. With that, John motioned for Jason to have a seat two tables over.

John had the kind of gaze that could look into your soul and see everything that was there from the beginning of time. It was both disconcerting and calming at the same time. Jason's curiosity about this guy was growing by the second. The waitress came to the table as they sat down and asked what she could bring Jason. He responded with, "Coffee please, with cream" and she was off to retrieve it. John started, "I understand that you met with Joe last week. He is quite a guy, isn't he?" "He really is," responded Jason. "He is like an old sage, or advisor that has already been there and done that. I really got a lot out of meeting with him." John said, "I have always enjoyed my meetings with him as well. And, he has sent me some pretty interesting characters over the years. Based on what I see, you will be another interesting one for me." "How do you mean," asked Jason. "I mean that I can see some of what is holding you back from your goals. There are some deliberate things that you will need to do in order to achieve what you desire. The good news is, I can help."

Jason smiled and the waitress walked up with a cup and two creamers in one hand and the pot of coffee in the other. She sat the cup on the table and filled it most of the way up, leaving room for the cream. She then topped off John's cup as well. She asked, "Can I get you two anything else?" John motioned toward Jason who said, "No thank you, just coffee for me." John agreed and they were back to their talk. Jason said, "You were saying that you could help me figure out what has been holding me back. I am very curious how you would do that." "To start with, I will be able to help you do that for yourself. All I do is let you know what is holding you back. You still have to decide whether or not you want to let go of them and move forward." Jason said, "You said them, not it. You said let go of them. What do you mean by that?" John smiled a knowing smile, took a sip of his coffee and responded. "I can help you by showing you which demons are attacking you and what to do about it. Before you pass judgment and think that I am crazy, hear me out." John could tell that Jason had immediately invited the demon of self-doubt and criticism back into his life. This was a very common one and one that was powerful in creating fear. In fact, this was one that John had to do battle with regularly in his own life. "Right now, Jason, you are experiencing doubt. You are hearing things like, 'This is stupid' and 'You need to get up and leave' and

'This will never work.' When you hear those things, you begin to doubt whether or not the person in front of you has any validity. Moreover, you begin to doubt whether or not you have any validity in doing what you do. If I were a betting man, I would bet that this particular demon, the demon of criticism and doubt has cost you hundreds of thousands of dollars in lost opportunity and a couple of good relationships along the way." Jason was a little shocked that he knew what he was thinking but was almost emotional at knowing that John was right. This demon of criticism and doubt, as he put it, had cost him lots of opportunities over the years. "So what is the demon of criticism and doubt?" John held up a hand to slow him down. "Before I get into that, I want to tell you that there are others. You seem to have several that keep battling for your acceptance. Your main fears seem to be criticism from others and doubt of self, the fear of poverty, and the fear of the loss of love." Jason had to remind himself to keep his jaw up. This guy was either good at guessing or he really knew what was going on in his head. Those were the three things that had plagued him for most of his life. Ever since he was young, he had worried about pleasing other people and keeping their approval. He had watched his dad's finances go up and down and had developed, what he referred to as, a stark raving terror of poverty. At times, he felt like he was so afraid of what others, particularly his family, would think about an idea of his that he would simply do nothing instead of something.

"Jason, I am going to work with you to understand the six demons of fear and to know how to control them. Perhaps more importantly, I am going to let Joe introduce you to some key people and key places that will show you what the consequences of giving in would be and other places and people that will show you what the benefits are of conquering these demons. What I have learned for sure is this… When I tell you something it means one thing. When you choose it for yourself, it means everything." Jason thought about that for a minute and said, "I would agree that it means so much more when I choose it for myself. How do I know that this is for real, though?" "You mean, how do you know I'm not tricking you?" "Well, yeah," said Jason. "You will know for yourself when you experience the demons and beat them. I still need to tell you who and what they are first. And then, you can decide for yourself whether you want to continue on this journey. Does that sound fair enough?" "That sounds fair to me," said Jason.

There are six demons that you will have to encounter and beat in order to achieve your goals in this life. Each one of them will come at you in a different way. Each one will try to trick you and convince you that it is you, not them, that is prodding in the wrong direction. Before I share their names, you need to understand that it is your burning desire and faith that will help you to beat them. You must have a burning desire to accomplish your goals and must know why those goals are critical to you. I would suggest that you pick up the book, Success: A 12-Step Program from Amazon.com. This will help you understand how to create that fire in your soul that will keep you going when your demons are trying to stop you. You have to build emotional energy in the right direction because the demons will do everything in their power to drain your energy from you and keep you from the path of success. So, are you willing to read and learn what is necessary to succeed?" "Yes I am," said Jason. John looked at him as if studying his soul and said, "We'll see."

"The first demon is known as "Dubium," or doubt. His objective is to make you see the things that you do wrong. He strives to make you doubt your direction, doubt yourself, and doubt your abilities. You will face him first. In order to succeed, you will need to beat him. He can be the weakest of the demons, but is often the one that others get stuck on.

The second demon is known as "Paupertas," or poverty. His objective is to create a fear of living in poverty. He needs only to get you to focus on poverty in order to make you attract that into your life. He is stronger than the first demon because you have been conditioned to measure your worth on your financial situation.

The third demon is known as "Aegritudinem," which means sickness. He strives to create a mental focus on your body failing. If he can get you to focus on physical pain, he can get you to give up your focus on your goals. People will often strive for attention through sickness without consciously realizing that they are focused on that.

The fourth demon is known as "Antiquis

Mortem," or old age and death. This demon will strive to beat you by creating a belief that you are too old to try, or that you are beyond your prime. His objective is to win by getting you to settle because it is too late for you. Around the age of 40, men in particular, begin to believe that they have lost their prime and can no longer compete in the game of life. This demon strives to plant a fear of your own mortality in your mind. He will try to create a fear that this mortality is the end, that there is nothing beyond this physical realm. He will attempt to convince you that there is no happiness or peace after this physical existence. He will also plant a fear that there is life after the physical realm, but it is hell and it is to be feared.

The fifth demon is incredibly powerful. She is known as "Nullus Amor" which means no love or loss of love. Her objective is to convince you that you will have nothing because you will achieve your goals but be left with no love in your life. She will work to convince you that your family, your friends, even your business associates will all turn on you and that you are the only person that you can trust."

The sixth and final demon is known as "Iratus" which means angry. This creature strives to keep you believing that you must be angry in order to be protected. It will keep the bad things in front of you and make you believe that you are a victim and must, therefore, be angry at your oppressors. It attempts to convince you that you cannot control your choices or your outcomes. It plants the idea that being angry and hateful is the only way to make others respect you. It's ultimate goal is to use you to drive away everyone that would love you. It is like a thief in the night. It comes to steal and destroy and it seeks to use you as its instrument of destruction.

Jason stared almost blankly forward at John. All he could think about was how intense the fear of facing these demons would be. "How do I face these demons, John? How do I beat them?" John let a slight smile curl up on both sides of his mouth. "I thought you would never ask." You will be given the opportunity to meet with someone who has been very successful at overcoming each of these demons in their life. You will meet with Joe and with a warrior in order to overcome each of them."

"How do I know that this is real?" John looked at him compassionately and then clasped his hand, the one connected to his coffee cup. Instantly, the room came alive and noises began to come from every direction. Jason could feel the challenges and the victories of each person that was in the café, as well as the people that walked by. He saw a greenish, well thing, or maybe a demon, that was attached to a man's back. He could tell that the demon was telling him that he would have a heart attack just like his father did. How could he know that, though? Jason tried to speak and ask John a question, but his mouth didn't seem to work. He looked across the room and saw a woman who was shaking her head, with a red demon on one side and bright white, well, an angel on the other side of her. The two figures seemed to be in an exchange through the woman, each pleading their case. The red demon kept telling the woman that all hope was lost and there was no way to make it out of this financial hole. The angel kept trying to comfort the woman. It was all so real.

Just then, John let go of Jason's hand and all of the noise, the demons, the angels, all of it was gone. "Where did it go?!" This was part question and part demand. Jason wanted to know where everything was and how to get it back. "That's my world, Jason. That is the world that is real and that is where the 6 demons of fear live. I needed you to know that what you are facing is real, but you can absolutely beat it." "Are you sure that I can beat it?" "I'm sure," said John. "Your journey has already begun, Jason. You will begin to encounter each of these demons in order and will have to beat them within the week. Your mentor and guides will help you. Once you conquer them, you will have the tools to succeed again and again. The demons never fully go away. They just get easier and easier to beat." "When will I start to see them, or encounter them?" John took a sip of coffee before answering. "You will begin to see them in the morning. Joe will introduce you to your guides and fellow warriors during each week's battle. You are ready when you believe that you are ready." Jason took a deep breath and said, "I'm ready." "Head home and relax for the rest of the day. Your real battle begins in the morning."

And with that, John tossed a $10 bill on the table and got up to leave. Jason sat there contemplating what he had just been told. He drank several more cups of coffee before finally getting up to leave almost an hour later. He left another $5 on the table just to be extra nice on the tip, since he had taken up the table for half of the morning. As he got into his car, he knew that this battle would be more than he had faced in the past but it would be worth it.

3 CRITICISM AND DOUBT

"What do you want?" "You know what I want Jason. I want to keep you from getting hurt. I want to protect you from what others will say about you if you try this. You're not ready. You don't have the skills that you need. I am sure you will some day, just not now. You don't want to be laughed at, do you? Jason was trying to keep this demon at bay. He had seen him over and over again throughout his life. For the past 20 years, this one had visited him the most. He had just not known that it was a demon before now. He had always assumed that it was his own self-talk. "I hate when people laugh at me. You know that!" Jason was staring at himself in the mirror and for the first time, imagining a demon sitting on his back and trying to shove thoughts into his head. Even though he knew this, it was still extremely tough to not accept the negative ideas. He could almost hear the demon saying to him, "That's why I want to help you Jason. You aren't good enough yet. Give it more time. You don't need all that pressure to make things happen right now. Wait until you are ready before you take a chance." Jason shook his head and tried to clear his mind. "What did John do to me?"

Jason had gotten an email from Joe, letting him know that they would be getting together with Emma at the café where they originally met. Jason had about 90 minutes to get ready and get there. He splashed some cold water on his face, then took a couple of deep breaths and shook his head one more time as if trying to rattle something loose. He got dressed, shaved, and drank a cup of coffee. He had the TV on in the background, just as a way to fill the space and keep him from thinking about the doubt that he seemed to be experiencing. He knew that this could be and probably was one of the demons that John had talked about. It didn't seem to make it any easier to deal with, though. When he finished his cup of coffee, he rinsed the mug and sat it on the dirty dish side of the sink.

Jason climbed into his car and headed out to see what he would learn today. What was it that he needed to know about this feeling that had been kicking his butt for 20+ years of his life? He turned on some classic rock and tried his best to lose himself in the music. Good music had always been a distractor for him and gave him some reprieve from his own thoughts.

Jason pulled in about 10 minutes early to the café and he could see Joe sitting in his booth, the same one that they met in last time. There was a lady there with him, which he assumed to be Emma. He got out of the car, grabbed his notebook from the back seat, checked how he looked in the reflection of the back window of his car, and then turned on his heels and headed into the café. Whatever he needed to learn, he would take it in and do his best to embrace the change.

"Hey Jason," Joe said as he stood up to shake his hand and greet him. Emma stood as well to meet him. "I'm Emma. Joe was just telling me about you and we were discussing how important this first plan of attack is." "Plan of attack," Jason asked with an inquisitive expression on his face. "Yes sir. If you want to win the game of life, you have to be ready to do battle every day with the things that would try to drag you down. You have to be ready to beat the doubt and criticism out of your life altogether." Jason had a slight grin on his face as he thought about the fire that existed in this rather short woman with reddish-blonde hair. "I don't think I would want to mess with you," said Jason. Emma let a smile spread across her face as she said, "I wouldn't even want to mess with me."

With that, they sat down and the waitress was there in just a few seconds. "Would you like a cup of coffee, hun? Jason looked up at the waitress and said, "Yes please." She headed off to grab a third mug for the table and the three of them looked at each other for a quiet moment. Joe was the first to speak. "Jason, I asked Emma to join us because she has some tremendous experience with doubt and criticism. She has helped more than a thousand people achieve greater heights in their lives by overcoming their own doubt and often the criticism of others. Some of the greatest overcomers that I have ever met say that they owe their success to this fireball." Joe made a motion towards Emma, whose face was turning slightly red now. "You're too kind." said Emma as she did a mock curtsy in her seat.

"What is it that you do," asked Jason looking straight at Emma. "I help people understand their potential, regardless of their circumstance. I take people and help them reshape their own minds, so that they live in a possibility world instead of an impossibility world." "So, are you like a motivational life coach?" Emma smiled at Jason's question. "No. I am a physical therapist. I work with people who have all types of physical opportunities." "Physical opportunities?" "Jason, when a person comes to me, they have been injured in some way. If they see that injury as a limitation on their potential, then they will live as if they have less to offer the world. Often times, the people that I work with will never be back to the person that they were or thought they were before the injury or stroke or heart attack or whatever they went through." Jason was intrigued. He remembered his short experience with rehabbing after he had a knee surgery in his early 20's from an injury. "When I went through rehab myself, I just thought that my therapist was possessed by sadistic evil spirits. They were mean, but they pushed me through the pain to be able to gain most of my knee's ability back." "I am never seen as possessed by, I believe you said 'sadistic evil spirits.' I help people see that they are now a newer version of themselves. I help them see that there is so much more to them than what happens to them." Emma took a drink of her coffee and then looked up and left, as if she was trying to remember something. She glanced over at Joe and then back to Jason.

"Let me tell you a story about Sara. She has encouraged me to use her story to encourage others and help them see that there is more to life than the things that happen to us." Jason looked at Emma and raised his eyebrows just slightly in anticipation of what Sara's story would be. He noticed that both John and Joe had used stories to make their point as well. People just seem to learn better when they can relate to an experience that someone else has already gone through.

The Story of Sara

Sara was a young lady that was full of life and energy at 19 years old. She had been a high school cheerleader and had always been very athletic. She had finished her first year in college and was back for the start of her second year. It was the second day back and classes had not started yet. Sara lived in the dorms and had the same roommate her Sophomore year that she did her Freshman year. Sara didn't drink, didn't smoke, and didn't party. I say that to make sure you understand that the story that I am about to tell you should not have happened to her. It wasn't fair and she didn't deserve to have anything bad happen.

Jason was thinking about the image of a young lady with the world in front of her who deserved to have a great life. He couldn't imagine what Emma was about to tell him had happened to Sara.

Sara went out to eat with a group of her friends that evening. I remember her telling me that they had gone to Chili's, which was her favorite restaurant, at least it was at that time. They had a great time at the restaurant, laughing and cutting up and talking about what the year was going to be like. They left the restaurant around 7:30 PM. They weren't out late. Sara was driving and there were 3 girls riding with her in her car. The trip back to the campus and to the dorm was about 2 miles, so not very far. That was one of the reasons that they liked to eat at Chili's. Two blocks before they got back to the campus, Sara was struck on the driver's side, right on her door, by a 20 year old young man who was drunk and driving his pickup. There were four people in the back of the pickup, all of whom were thrown from the back. These boys were also students at the college. Sara doesn't remember the next two weeks after the impact. She just remembers looking to her left as she went through the green light and seeing a boy driving the truck at a high rate of speed and looking backwards out of his back window at the people in the bed of his truck.

Jason imagined the fear that he would have had if he had been the person being struck and the regret that he would have if he had been the young man driving drunk. He had driven under the influence of alcohol several times when he was younger and was now so thankful that he had never caused anything like this. Even though he didn't know the outcome, he knew that it couldn't be good.

Sara woke up in the hospital almost two weeks later. The doctors had kept her in a medically induced coma in order to keep the swelling down on her brain. When they brought her out of the coma, Sara had her entire family around her. She was the oldest of four kids and the only girl. Her parents were there and all three of her brothers were there. She could only remember seeing the pickup coming at her and couldn't remember anything else. In some ways, she says that not remembering is a blessing. All three of her friends survived. The one in the back seat, right behind her had a concussion and a broken arm and several cuts that required stitches. The passenger in the front seat walked away with bruises and the girl in the back passenger side had whiplash and a broken left wrist. The drunk driver broke his jaw, both arms, one leg, and his nose. Three of the young men in the back of the truck, amazingly, walked away after being thrown out. The fourth one died from a broken neck. He was brand new to the college and had just met those boys that day. Sara lost her left leg, at the knee. It had been crushed so severely that there was nothing that the doctors could do to save it. She had several broken ribs that made breathing difficult and painful. She had cuts all over the left side of her face and had a broken left hand. Amazingly, she responded with, "I am so blessed to be alive." Her family was grateful to still have her and they brought her home to heal. Sara had no idea that her leg was missing at this point. Shortly after waking up, she asked her mom to scratch her left foot because it itched really bad. Her mom began to cry as she tried to explain to Sara that her leg had been amputated at the knee. It is common for people to have ghost pains as well as itches on parts of their limbs have been amputated. The nerves have not adjusted to realize that the limb is missing.

Jason could feel himself welling up with emotions, imagining what it would have been like to be in that position. He couldn't imagine going from being athletic and young and having the world in front of him and then realizing that he would not be athletic, or walk on his own, or live in the way that he had known for the last 19 years.

Sara spent the first couple of weeks, after waking up, just adjusting to the idea that life would be different. As the thought of never walking without assistance sank in, she began to doubt what the rest of her life would be like. She began to doubt that any man would want to date her or marry her because, in her mind, she was no longer a whole woman. I got her for rehab work 4 weeks after the crash. I remember the day that I met her. Her scrapes and cuts were beginning to heal and her bones had begun to really mend as well. She had not been fitted for a prosthetic leg, but I was to introduce her to the idea in our first session. I may not remember the exact exchange, but it was something like this…

"Hello Sara, my name is Emma and you are going to love me over the next several months." Sara looked at me for about 10 seconds and then finally extended her right hand to shake mine. Her question that she asked me told me that self-doubt had really set in and she was imaging that others were criticizing the way that she looked, even if they hadn't actually said anything. "Nice to meet you, but what is the point? My life is over." I looked at her and responded with, "Thank God Sara 1.0 is done because Sara 2.0 is gonna change the world! You have nothing but opportunity in front of you. You can be anyone, do anything, and have anything that you are willing to work for." Sara started crying. She wept for the better part of 10 minutes as I knelt in front of her and held her hand. Her parents had been trying to keep her at home and take care of her. They didn't want her to go back to school, to the place where danger existed. The idea of not being capable of being on her own had lead to her being depressed and feeling mostly hopeless. Nobody had told her that life was still full of possibility. "Are you willing to work, Sara?" I finally asked her after the crying stopped. "Will I be able to walk?" "You

will be able to run if you are willing to work at it," I told her. "Then I will work as hard as I can. I just worry that I will never be the woman that I used to be." "Sara, you have been given an opportunity to inspire others, to change this world, and to make a real difference. I know that it doesn't seem like it now. It seems like life is unfair and you have had things taken away from you. It can be whatever you decide to make it though. It can be the end of everything that you knew and the end of opportunity, or it can be the beginning of a new version of you. I promise you this, Sara. What you get out of life from this point forward is completely up to you. You are in a bad situation but you are not a bad person. You can choose to define yourself or to allow the circumstances of life define you. The demons of doubt will try to convince you that what is going on in your life, your challenges, your struggles, that these are the things that make up the whole of who you are. You can allow these demons into your mind or you can make them leave. It is a choice." Sara sat there for several minutes, just staring straight forward, deep in thought. Finally she responded, "What do I need to do to send those demons where they belong?" Then, she broke into a smile and lifted her head. She looked me straight in the eyes and said, "Let's do this!"

"I have never had a patient that was more driven to overcome their challenges from that point forward. This young lady was not going to allow life to get her down. The day that she decided to take control of her opinion of herself and not allow others, including her family, to define her, was the day that she won her battle. These demons of self-doubt and criticism want to take control of you, even if you have not been hit by a drunk driver as a beautiful young lady. These demons want control of you. They want to control executives, car washers, moms and dads, and anyone and everyone that they can. Make no mistake, it is control that the demons seek. When they can control a person through the fear of criticism and by creating self-doubt, they can keep a person from achieving what they are capable of." Sara finished up with her explanation and looked thoughtfully at Jason. "Jason, what doubt and criticism do you have about yourself that is holding you back?"

Jason knew that he was there to learn, but he had not anticipated being asked to bear his soul. He wasn't ready for the question. He took a sip of his coffee to create a pause so that he could think of his answer. He knew immediately that he doubted himself and that he was guilty of beating himself up regularly, but he didn't know how to answer the question. So, he just began, "Well, I guess… I guess I would have to say that I look at people who are rich and successful and I look at people who are poor and unsuccessful in the same way." "What do you mean," asked Emma. "I mean, I don't see myself as being capable of either of those extremes. I see myself as a middle of the road person. Every time I start to win in life and in business, I seem to find a way to pull myself back to the middle. Every time I begin to fail, lose business or money or anything like that, I find a way to pull myself back up to the middle. I doubt that I have the capacity to go anywhere but here. And, every time I start to go outside of my comfort zone, I start hearing this voice in my head telling me that I am going in the wrong direction, that I don't deserve that path, or that I am not good enough."

Jason was a little shocked that he had just spilled

his guts about that. He normally tried to keep up a solid front about who he wanted to world to see. He normally tried to hide his shortcomings. There was just something about Emma that made it almost impossible to lie about who he really was. "Jason, you are not so different than most people. Just like with Sara's story, you have a blueprint of who you are. The simple truth is that your blueprint of you is how you see yourself and what you will tend to live into. Have you ever seen a blueprint to a building?" Jason sat up and got a picture of a blueprint in his mind. He hadn't seen but a couple of sets of blueprints, but he knew what they looked like. "I do. I have seen a couple of sets," Jason replied. "So, is the blueprint of a building the actual building itself?" Jason thought about Emma's question for a second and replied, "No. The blueprint is more of a map for how the building should be put together and how it is put together." "So, if you were to change a blueprint, and you had a full-time construction crew that implemented any changes that you accepted, would the building change?" "Sure, if you change a blueprint and someone makes those changes happen, then the building changes too."

"Here's the thing Jason. Your blueprint of life is not life itself. It is simply a representation of what your life is now. So when you say that you can't see yourself going towards success or away from success, you are saying that your blueprint is your actual representation of reality, as it stands now." Jason responded, "That's correct. This is my current reality." "You can think of the demons of criticism and doubt like you would think of a construction foreman that doesn't want to work, nor does he want others to work outside of the accepted parameters. The thing is, you are the architect. You control the blueprint. You control it to the point that you can simply accept a new rule for your life and then the demons can't prevent you from achieving the new blueprint of reality." "So, if I can conceive and believe that I am a different person, you are saying that I will actually become that different person?" asked Jason. "That's correct. I would even take it one step further. You can't help but be the person that you truly believe that you are. You must have belief in who you are, though. The second that you have a new belief, you have a new blueprint, which means that you have a new reality!" Emma was getting revved up now. She was very excited about the message that she was sharing with Jason. This was obviously very important to her and had obviously shaped her life.

"Jason, what if Sara would have accepted the blueprint of being helpless that several of her loved ones had presented her with? Where would she be?" "I suppose she would be helpless right now. We are who we believe we are." Jason sat back and let this reality sink into his subconscious mind. He thought about the number of times that he had simply not accepted the reality he wanted, but had believed the wrong reality that he was in. Jason looked right at Emma and asked, "So, are you saying that I build the reality of my life from the blueprint that I create?" "That's right, Jason," said Emma. "The crazy part is that you get to choose any blueprint that you want. Everyone gets to. It's just that the demons of criticism and doubt sit on your shoulders and whisper their ideas for your blueprint. The second that you stop accepting their negative influence and send them away, they have no power or control over you. The truth is, they never could control you unless you allowed them to control you." Jason took a couple of sips of his coffee and imagined the number of times in his life that he had allowed these demons to whisper their truth, not his, into his mind. "I have wasted so much of my life with the wrong blueprint," said Jason. "Most people have," said Emma. "Most people have allowed those lies to rule their life instead of believing that they were created for greatness. Remember what I said earlier about action, Jason?" "Yes, I do. You said that whatever blueprint I accept and take action to construct is the one that I will get." "That's right. You have to first have the belief about the blueprint for your life and then you have to work as hard as it requires to get you there. Most people will run back to their demons of doubt when the work becomes hard. They will trash their perfect blueprint for an imperfect one." "Are you saying that people intentionally become less than they are capable of being?" "Of course I am, Jason. I am saying that people choose an easy blueprint because it requires less work." Jason thought about how many times he had not done what would have made him successful. "You're right, Emma. I know that I have done the very same thing. I have chosen the path of least resistance because that looked like the sure bet. I didn't want to risk failing, so I did it intentionally. I just didn't realize that I was choosing failure by accepting the wrong blueprint for my life."

"Jason, I want to give you some homework that will help the two little guys that were attached to you, your demons that is, to lose their grip and fall by the wayside." "Let me have it," Jason said with enthusiasm. "I want those boys to get their butts kicked by my new blueprint." Emma said, "It sounds like you are one step ahead of me. Your homework is to write out the perfect blueprint for your life. I want you to write it out in the first person and present tense, though." "What do you mean? I'm not living my perfect life, so how can I write it in present tense?" "What I mean is that you will pick the date of one year in to the future and then write out what your life is already like at that point. Your mind will accept the present tense, not the future or the past. If you state your blueprint in future terms, it will always stay in the future. You need to state it as if it already exists. To get your mind to accept it, you simply state the current date as one year into the future." "is there anything else," asked Jason. "No. That is it. Change is not actually complicated. It is instantaneous. It is based on the accepted blueprint that exists for you in your own mind." "That sounds great! I will write it out and describe as much of my life as possible, one year from today."

Emma stood up and stuck her hand out to shake Jason's. "I am counting on you to follow through. When the demons of doubt and criticism want to visit, simply pull out your blueprint and read it out loud. You need to reinforce this new and accepted belief as often as you can."

Jason shook Emma's hand and dropped a $20

bill on the table. "Thank you Emma! My blueprint is my own personal reality. I am going to make it incredible!"

Jason walked to his car, got in and took out his notebook. He wanted to jot down a few notes to remember how to beat the demons of doubt and criticism.

The demons of doubt and criticism only have the amount of power that I give them.

These are the demons that whisper self-doubt into my mind. In order to condition myself to be stronger against them, I need to…

1. *Establish a definite blueprint of the reality that I want and accept it.*
2. *Say positive things to myself at all times. If something messes up, remember that it is an event and it is not me.*
3. *Every successful person started as a person who accepted that they were a successful person that just hadn't received their reward yet.*

4 POVERTY

John had driven through this neighborhood before, but he had never stopped. He could see the hunched over demon in every house. It would drag people down and cloud their minds. It seemed to have an incredible power to prevent people from bettering themselves. It had claws that looked like hooks. As he sat at the corner looking into the souls that existed inside each house, he was saddened by how deep the claw hooks of poverty were into the souls inside. He simply wasn't able to watch from a distance anymore. He knew that people would criticize him. He knew that a number of people would reject him. It didn't matter. It wasn't him that had to be ready. It was God as a part of him that would lead the way. Today would be the day that he did battle with the demon of poverty. He needed to be ready for this next meeting with Joe and Jason. Joe knew how difficult this was going to be for him to stomach, and he knew it as well. He had to get a grip on this in order to help make change happen. He had to understand how to remove those awful claws from people's souls and minds.

After a good hour of driving around the neighborhood, John headed out toward the café where Joe would be waiting for him. He and Joe were going to get together before Jason joined them. Joe had said that he would have one other person with him as well. He wasn't sure who that was at this point, but he knew that Joe knew what he was doing. Joe had done this same process for several other people that he knew of. All of them were now incredibly successful in all areas of their lives. The drive helped John to really clear his head and prep for the meeting. This demon was one of the strongest he had ever done battle with. It was one that regenerated itself from one generation to the next to the next, all with people believing that poverty was simply their fate and that there was nothing that they could do about it.

The road was curvy and the sun was just cresting as it rose that morning. Every now and then, when the car was angled just right, the sun shone so brightly through the windshield that John had to squint hard to see where he was. He made it to the café safely with a few minutes to spare. Luckily, Joe loved the café that was definitely "off the beaten path." Even though he was early, Joe was already inside at his usual table, already sipping his coffee. John parked his car, grabbed a notebook and started to head inside. As he did, he noticed a woman sitting at the table with Joe. She looked to be around 30 or 35 years old. As he was studying her and noticing the spiritual scars that seemed to be on her soul, he slowed his pace. He could see what looked like, well, like hook marks in multiple parts of her soul. He recognized them as the same marks that he had seen that morning as he drove through the slums of the city. This was a woman who no longer had the demon of poverty, but still had the scars to prove where she had come from. He picked his pace back up and went into the café and over to their table.

Joe stood up and extended his hand to welcome John. "John, great to see you man. I want to introduce you to Sam. Sam this is John. He is the seer that I was telling you about." Samantha, who went by Sam, stood up and extended her hand with a warm and confident smile. "It's a pleasure to meet you John. Joe has told me quite a bit about your incredible abilities. I would imagine that can be both a gift and a curse, depending on who you are with." Sam smiled again. She seemed to know that the challenge of seeing the truth about people was not always sunshine and roses. It could be a real burden to know the truth about a person but not always know how to help them. "Sam, you are so right. Sometimes this gift is incredible and sometimes it is frustrating because of not knowing how to help. That is one of the reasons that I stay as connected to Joe as I possibly can. His gift is that of the wisdom of knowing what path to take to help people get where they need to be and where they want to be." With that, all three of them took a seat. The waitress now knew what John liked and was already on her way with his coffee. John doctored the cup the way he liked, two creams and three sugars, stirred the contents together well, and then took a sip.

"Joe, you had suggested that I drive through the slums this morning. You know that the demon of poverty is my least favorite of the six that plague people and keep them from success. I am assuming that you had a purpose for having me see such pain." John lifted his cup and took a sip while raising his eyebrows in a questioning manner. "Of course, John; you know that I wouldn't have you see that pain if I didn't have a purpose for it. Sam is one of the folks that I met a couple of years ago and could see potential in. I helped her understand the truth about what was keeping her down. Even though I can't see what you see, I had known you long enough to know what was keeping her down. Once I taught her about the blueprints that Emma taught Jason about this last week, I taught her about compensation. This principle of compensation is how anyone can pull themselves out of poverty, coupled with the principle of the self-blueprint, that is." John was focused now. He had spent a lot of time doing battle directly with the demon of poverty on behalf of others, but it seemed to keep coming back.

"What is the principle of compensation?" John was still looking directly at Joe when he asked the question. Joe took a sip of coffee and motioned his head to the right, toward Sam. "Sam, why don't you take this one. You can be brief because you will need to teach this to Jason as well when he gets here." Sam smiled with confidence and pride. She was excited to be a part of helping someone else learn the way that she did.

"Well, to put it as simply as possible, the principle of compensation says that for everything that we do, there is a result. What I put in, I get out. Think of the duality of nature. If you are to magnetize the end of a needle, the other end of the needle will have the opposite magnetism. What is the opposite of dark or tall or left or cold?" John was trying to make sure that he kept up. "That would be light, short, right, and hot." Sam wasn't actually expecting an answer and it made her chuckle a little. "That's right. The big question is, can one exist without the other?" John said, "I suppose it can't. Without the duality of one, the other wouldn't exist." "Good," Sam said. "You're right that they need each other to be able to be defined. Focused energy creates motion. It is this energy that is the duality of success. Success cannot exist without the duality of focused energy. You push yourself so that success can pull you."

John sat back in his chair with both of his hands curled loosely around his coffee cup. The expression on his face said it all. It was so simple, yet so elusive to most. Every choice leads to an action. Every action yielded its duality of a result. Without this principle of compensation, nothing would exist. It made perfect sense. The demon of poverty convinced people of the action of waiting. It convinced them to wait for something to be done for them instead of doing for themselves. After all, waiting was an action. Waiting was a pull. The duality of a pull is a push. This meant that success was pushing these people away instead of pulling them in. "That makes perfect sense Sam. A pull will result from a push and a push will result from a pull. Everything in nature works in harmony, just as God intended it to. God provides a field of pure potential for anyone. What we do in that field is up to us and is based on the choices that we make." "That's correct," said Sam. She added, "I made a series of choices early on in my life that perpetuated the poverty that my parents were in. I didn't want to learn success. I didn't want to learn discipline. I wanted to pull, as you stated it, and I was pushed away from success and victory. My parents wanted something better for me, but they didn't know how to get me there. When I was 16 years old, I had a baby on the way, because that was what my blueprint told me was normal for girls in my neighborhood. I dropped out of school and started looking for a job. I found a job as a waitress at a small café that was a little out of the way, but the bus ran there. Joe was the gentleman that suggested that I apply. He had walked up to me at a convenience store and told me that I looked like I would make a fantastic waitress at this place." John asked, "At which place was it?" Sam smiled and motioned around the room with her hands. "It was this very café that he suggested I apply and I was hired on the spot. I was late to work the first several days, until the manager, Steven, sat me down and explained the principle of compensation to me. I knew that I needed to have this job because I was about to have two lives to support. He made me feel that I could be anyone that I wanted to be if I was willing to work for it. I started pouring coffee for this man." Sam pointed at Joe with her cup. "He would take time to visit with me each day that he was here. He was always meeting someone, but always had time before they got here. He expanded on the concept of creating a blueprint for my life and helped me understand that the principle of compensation would lead to my success or my failure. I am 25 years old now and have a 2nd grader that is about to turn 9 years old. He and I are doing great. I own a small business and have four employees that work their tails off to make us all successful. I owe it to the lessons that I learned while working in this very café. For that, I will always be grateful. Because of the success that I earned, I have been able to continue to push myself forward and create a pull for those who are also working to push themselves forward. We create a wake, like a boat does, when we accelerate our success. This makes it easier and easier for others to succeed. America has been a country of success because of the amount of self-drive and personal pushing that has happened. This makes it easier and easier for others to follow along that same path." Sam stopped herself and smiled. Joe was smiling as well. She continued, "I am getting on my soapbox now. The more each person works to become successful in a neighborhood, the more contagious the choice of the principle of compensation becomes."

Now it was Joe's turn to speak. "John, I need you and Sam to work together with Jason on this one. This is a really big deal. Jason has a strong fear of poverty. Fear is a negative attractor. It attracts the thing that the negative energy is focused on. The duality of fear is faith. Faith attracts positive energy and positive forces. Because this world is a world of duality, Jason needs to understand the duality of fear and faith, failure and success, poverty and abundance. Can you work with Sam to help her?" Joe already knew the answer but loved hearing people commit to make a difference. "You know that I will be glad to do whatever I need to Joe. Sam and I will help Jason see his choices clearly." John finished off his cup of coffee and as he was sitting the cup down, the waitress was there to fill it back up. The service was impeccable here, which made it much easier to stay focused on the change that mattered.

The Hooks

Jason made it to the café and joined the three that were already in place. He wasn't sure what was in store for him today, but he knew that it would be good. He had already learned so much about the world that existed outside of his normal sight. Seeing John there, he knew that another lesson would be forthcoming. No matter what, Jason had to figure out how to move himself forward, out of the rut that his life seemed to be perpetually stuck in.

"Welcome Jason," Joe said with a great big smile. "Let me introduce you to Sam. She is one of my students and has really done some incredible things with her life. She has gone from poverty to small business success because of her beliefs. I have asked her to give you some lessons on what creates your faith in self and overcomes any hooks that poverty can possibly get in your mind.

"Before that, I wanted to ask you a question,

though." Joe took a sip of his coffee and leaned forward intently. He was creating the full intensity of his question in Jason's mind. "What did you learn about the demons of doubt and criticism?" Jason was ready for this. He had been focusing on his blueprint and on his self-affirmations. "Well Joe, I learned that doubt and criticism only have the amount of power that I allow them to have. Just saying that I don't want them to have power over me, though, won't cut it. I have to build some layers of protection for myself." "How do you do that?" Joe asked. "I'm glad you asked," said Jason. Sam and John chuckled a little. Jason was developing more confidence already. Before learning about how to deal with doubt and criticism, he would have hesitated on such a direct question from someone like Joe. "There are three steps as I see it," continued Jason.

1. *Establish a definite blueprint of the reality that I want and accept it as my truth. I have made this easier by writing out bits of that reality on notecards and placing them all over my house and car so that I reinforce them regularly.*
2. *Say positive things to myself at all times. If something messes up, I will remember that those are events. I will learn from them, become stronger, and move myself closer to my reality.*
3. *And finally, I remember that every successful person started out as a person who accepted their blueprint and knew that they had simply not been rewarded yet for their success.*

"It sounds like you really let those lessons sink in Jason," commented Sam. She continued, "I don't think that I could have said that any better myself."

Sam said this with a great big and very confident smile.

Jason was excited about what he was going to learn this time. The lessons on criticism and doubt had already made his view of reality much better. He knew that each lesson would take him closer and closer to his goal of living the life that he imagined. His excitement was pretty apparent, based on the fact that he was leaning in and seemed to be floating a few inches off of his chair. He was so ready to learn the next lesson, he asked, "So what do I get to learn today that will make my life more fulfilling?"

This time, John broke into a smile and answered, "You get to learn about the hooks of poverty and how to keep them out of your life." Jason wasn't actually expecting to talk about poverty, but he knew that this was an intense fear that he had in his life. His stomach started to swirl a little with nervousness. "Don't freak out Jason. You have been battling this demon hard in your life. Your spirit keeps dodging him. He sinks his hooks in, you pry him off, and he keeps coming back. Unlike the other demons, he doesn't have claws. He has hooks that dig in deeper and more intensely than the others. He can't be pushed away as easily. I can see in your spirit that this is one of your bigger fears." John stared at Jason and waited for a response. Jason was only thinking that he wished that this seer, John, wasn't peering into his soul. He could feel himself slipping into self-doubt. He screamed in his mind and reminded himself that he was in control of his thoughts. He shoved the demons of doubt and criticism to the side and focused on what needed to be done. "I have always had a fear of poverty. I worry that one day I will wake up and my life will crumble around me and I will end up on the street, begging for food." Sam jumped in, "Jason, would you mind if I asked you a few questions?"

Jason was imagining himself in poverty and Sam's question jolted him out of that bad vision. "Sure Sam. Ask me anything that you want. I just want this feeling to go away." Sam patted his hand which was attached to his coffee cup and resting on the table. "Ok Jason, I am going to ask you several questions that will reshape your picture right now. Does that sound good?" "Yes, it does." replied Jason. John and Joe were sitting back in their chairs and letting Sam work her magic. She was incredible at reshaping a person's vision of reality. She had been very successful at creating new roadmaps of reality through her questioning. "Here we go. Jason, I want you to close your eyes and imagine yourself in the poverty that you fear the most. Get as clear of a picture as you can." Jason had closed his eyes and his face seemed to wince as he pictured himself in poverty and despair. "Now, I want you to tell me where the picture of you is. In other words, is it in the upper right hand corner of your thoughts, the lower left hand corner, the center, or somewhere else?" Jason thought about it for a minute and with an inquisitive expression on his face said, "It is in the upper right-hand corner of my mind." "Good," Sam said. "Now, we are going to adjust the image a bit. Keep the picture clear in you mind." "Got it," said Jason with his eyes still closed. Sam continued, "Is the image in black and white or in color?" Jason could immediately tell that it was in black and white and so he said, "Black and white." "What I want you to do, Jason, is turn the dial for color in your mind and add color to the picture. Make the colors very bright and vivid." Jason did and Sam could see the expression soften on Jason's face. "Is that better or worse?" Jason responded, "Better, definitely better." "Good," Sam said, "Now, is the image in first person or third person? In other words, are you observing the scene from outside or are you looking through your own eyes?" "I am watching this from outside. It seems like it is outside of my control." "Alright, now I want you to change the perspective, Jason. I want you to switch to a first person view. Put yourself into your body in the image and look out of your own eyes. Is it better or worse?" Jason was astonished at the change in his emotional state with each change in the image. "It's better again." Jason even smiled a little now. "Good job Jason," Sam continued. "Now, is the image large or is it small?" Jason responded, "large." "Okay, I want you to push the image of poverty out into the distance. I want you to push it half the length of a football field." "Okay, that makes it better again," said Jason. "Good, now let's push it a little further. Take it the entire length of a football field." Jason did and his expression continued to soften. "That's better again Sam!" Jason was getting excited by the prospect of killing this demon off in his mind. "Now, Jason, I want you to take the image of you in poverty as far away as you can where you can still see just a speck of the image. Move it at about 10 miles per hour away from you in your mind so that you are keeping tabs on it. When you have it down to the size of a speck, I want you to see yourself as a giant that can reach out and touch the speck." Jason was amused by the idea of being a giant and it felt good. "Now Jason, the demon of poverty is a tiny chip of ice in your mind. It is there and it is trying to chill off your drive for success and the results that you are pursuing, but it is now in perspective for you. As the giant that you are, I want you to picture a giant stove on the left hand side of your mind, the opposite side from where you saw the poverty." Jason was creating a great image of an old-fashioned wood stove that was stoked up and ready for cooking. "Got it," said Jason. "Okay, now with your giant hand, I want you to reach out and grab that tiny speck known as poverty and move it over the hot stove. When you are ready, drop the speck of ice onto the hot stove and make a sizzling sound to mimic what it sounds like when that hits the stove top." Jason was chuckling a little as he did this, but he followed through. He grabbed the speck between his right thumb and middle finger and moved it toward the stove top. He looked at the hot stove and instead of just letting go of the speck of demon ice, he made a slight downward tossing motion to indicate that he had tossed the speck directly onto the stove top. He then made the pssssss sound that he imagined a speck of ice frying on a hot stove would make. "Very good," said Sam. Now, when you think of poverty, what comes to mind?" Jason didn't hesitate when he said, "I feel in control, like it's nothing but an irritating chip of ice that I can fry at any time. I don't feel afraid!" Jason's eyes were open now and he was looking at the other people at the table.

Sam never got tired of seeing people overcome a fear with this technique. She asked Jason, "Do you think that you could do that same process if you somehow or another start being afraid of poverty again in the future?" "Sure, that was easy," said Jason. "When we are afraid, we hold the image of that fear in a specific path in our mind. We have a neuro-pathway to the fear. We have worn down the grass and pounded a path that is easy for our mind to follow. In order to get around that pathway, we simply have to develop an alternate route for our thoughts. We have to change our thought patterns and go the direction of success and confidence instead of the direction of the demons that hold us back. Does that make sense to you Jason?" Not only did Jason nod his head, the others at the table were nodding in agreement as well.

"I can see why poverty has stronger hooks than the others," said Jason. "Poverty is literally a pathway that guides our thoughts. It is the path itself that is holding us back." Now Sam was a little impressed. "That's right Jason. Poverty is a neuro-pathway. It is a demon that doesn't just whisper in your ear. It is a demon that serves as bumpers in your mind to keep your thoughts going toward failure and destruction. It takes a technique like you just went through to lower the guardrails that were installed." Jason said, "I guess you could say it was like bumper bowling, you know where they have those guards that pop up in the gutters at the bowling alley. Even if you throw a bad ball, the bumpers keep it in the lane. Except in this case, the bumpers are preventing you from hitting the pins." "I love it," said Sam. "That is a great image of what this demon does, when we let him." Paupertas is a tricky little devil, Jason. You will need to destroy his pathway completely. This will likely take half a dozen times of messing up the path that he has worn in your mind. Are you willing to persist at erasing his path as many times as it takes, Jason?" Jason had no doubt in his mind when he answered, "Though he may attack me again and again, I will keep destroying his path until it is overgrown with so much power that there would be no way for him to even find a path again in my mind!"

Everyone at the table nodded with pleasure, knowing that Jason would indeed destroy the pathway of Paupertas. Joe and John never tired of hearing the process of re-patterning thoughts. They had used the same techniques in their own lives to create pathways to success and to build solid roadblocks to failure by eliminating those pathways altogether.

The conversation seemed very light now, knowing that a new path to success had been formed. The small group bantered back and forth about business and life and family and what the possibilities of the future really were. It was the first time that Jason had really just joked around with any of the folks in the group. Things had been pretty serious, leading up to this point. It felt good. He felt that he was becoming a part of the success dream-team. He liked it. In fact, he loved it. He would focus on the lessons that he had learned and would put them into practice daily. After 20 or so minutes of fun and simple conversation, it was Joe that said it was time to head out. Everyone threw a few dollars onto the table for their coffee, except for Jason. Jason grabbed a $50 bill and tossed it onto the table. "Something inside of me told me to leave $50," he announced to the group. "Jason, that voice that you heard is a very important voice. Always listen to it and follow the positive direction that it will lead you. I am incredibly excited that your guide has arrived!" Joe offered no additional information. He left it at that. Jason knew, somehow, that this guide would be a critical component of the rest of his journey to success.

The waitress came by the table and picked up the money, just as the group was leaving. That morning, she had been trying to figure out how to afford to pay for the groceries that she and her family needed. She had figured that if she could make $50 in tips today, she would be alright. The total amount of money that was on the table totaled up to $50.01 in tips and the rest covered the coffees. Her eyes welled up with a layer of tears at the thought that someone or something out there was looking out for her and wanted her to be taken care of. She wiped away the tears of thankfulness, put the money in her apron, and headed off to do her job cheerfully. She was going to be alright. She was going to make it.

5 SICKNESS

Jason knew that it wasn't sickness itself that was the demon. That was simply a result. He knew that when a person's soul is out of sync with God, it is the fear of sickness that takes over. This demon pushed people to manufacture illness in order to receive medicine, to be treated, or to receive comfort that fixes something that is not actually the problem. This demon would push people to skip the sleep that they needed and wear themselves down in the pursuit of, well of happiness. The problem was that most people weren't finding happiness. Instead, they were finding sickness. This was the objective of the demon in the first place, to find ways to wear people down physically so that they would begin to focus on what was wrong instead of what was right. The demon of sickness was in control of too much of America's soul.

Jason had never really struggled with being sick or

even with the desire for attention through sickness. It wasn't something that ever seemed to distract him, other than when he was worn out from working too much. It was in those times of exhaustion that his body would shut him down so that he would rest. He knew that he needed to be more balanced in order to keep his mind and his body sharp, and to keep himself on track. This was something that he had begun disciplining himself to do a few years back, and he had found that he was much more in tune with where he was supposed to go than when he was tired. His big challenge was that he had a couple of friends that seemed to really embrace the idea of sickness. They embraced it so much that they had significantly more treatments of every kind than anyone else that he knew. In explaining the term, hypochondriac to his friend Steven when they were teenagers, Steven responded, "Oh crap, I have that." Steven had somehow found a way to successfully contract the flu, need multiple eye surgeries, and absorb the illnesses of others if he came within 100 feet of them. This had lead to the point of Steven not being very productive when it came to work.

The problem that Steven had went further, though. He was not producing at work because he felt bad. He felt bad because he was under constant attack and embraced his own defeat. He embraced his defeat because he had an image of himself that indicated he was being defeated by illnesses. When Steven did work, he would get mad at his boss for not recognizing that it was his illness that made him weak, not himself. His coworkers didn't understand that there was nothing that he could do about his situation, at least not in his own mind. Jason knew that this had to be the next lesson that he was to learn. He just knew that it was the demon of sickness that was the next challenge for him to hit head on. Jason had lost another friend of his to very strange illnesses that seemed to simply appear for this person. They were a lot like Steven's, and he just kept getting sick over and over and over again. The doctors couldn't find anything actually wrong with him. Despite the fact that he had test after test after test done, nobody could figure it out. So, the doctors did what most doctors do. They treated his symptoms. One medication fixed one problem and created another. Another medicine fixed the problem induced by the first medicine and then created another. This kept going and going. Eventually, his body was an experiment in chemical warfare. He was on so many medicines that his ability to think clearly was just, just gone.

After five years of over-medication, his body shut down. He never fulfilled a grand purpose on this earth. He never wrote a book, built a business, started a family, composed a symphony, authored a play, or anything that may have been inside of him. Jason was there a couple of days before his friend died. He told Jason that his greatest regret was that he let the illnesses control him. He didn't take hold of his life and live every second of it to the fullest. He never did the things that he had hoped to do when he was young. He urged Jason to beat any illness that came his way. He urged him to take control of his thoughts and look for the good in the world, regardless of the amount of bad that was hitting him in the face. This was a fascinating piece of advice from someone who never did what he was suggesting. It was fascinating because it caught Jason off guard. He knew that his friend was serious. He knew that his words meant more than most words would mean because he was at the end. When most people are at the end of their lives and they can sense it, they speak truth because they have nothing left to hide and nothing left to gain. They are simply raw and open.

Jason didn't want the same fate to come of his friend Steven. He wanted him to figure out how to live fully in spite of anything that came his way. He wanted him to understand something that nobody else had ever explained to him, least of all his parents. Steven had a choice. He had a choice as to how he viewed the world. Even if he didn't have a choice about being sick or being in perfect health, he had a choice about how he handled it. It wasn't the weekend yet, but he was ready to talk to Joe and wanted to see if John could join them. He needed to know how to approach his friend and how to help him overcome this demon. He grabbed his phone and dialed Joe.

"Hey Joe, it's Jason." Joe seemed to always be warm and open when Jason talked to him. "Hey Jason, how are you? How is the battlefield?" "Funny you should ask, Joe. I think I have found the next enemy that must be conquered for a person to live a full and rich life." Joe was intrigued. He knew that Jason had found his inner guide, but didn't know if he would listen to it or not. "Which enemy would that be, Jason?" "I believe that the next demon that I will learn about is the demon of sickness!" Jason was fired up about this. "How do you know?" Joe asked the question out of curiosity and intrigue and not out of mistrust. "Well," Jason said, "I was drinking my coffee this morning before I got my day started and I simply opened myself up to hear whatever I needed to hear. As I sat there, clearing my mind and living fully in the moment, I had an image of my friend Steven, who struggles with sickness." "Oh yeah, what kind of sickness," asked Joe. "If he has heard about it, read about it, or walked near it, he gets it." Jason used a little bit of sarcasm in his last statement. He continued, "Even when he was young, he would think that he was getting all kinds of illnesses. He would think he was getting malaria, and then whooping cough, and then shingles, and then a tumor, and on and on. He seemed to go out of his way to be ill. His mom was the same way. The only time that he got attention from his mom was if his illness was worse than hers. I don't know for sure if that is why he was sick, but it seems logical to me."

Joe thought about it for a minute and then said, "It could be that he was seeking attention from his mom and that is why he invited the sickness in. It could be that he is actually that sick. It could be that he allowed sickness in and then liked the result that he got from having the illness. A lot of people will take attention from a doctor when they don't get attention from a spouse or from their family." Jason jumped in, "Is sickness the result of an attack, just like poverty or self-doubt?" "Most of the time it is. We have a lot of manufactured illness in the United

States, Jason. We have illnesses that drug companies continuously manufacture so that they can sell the heck out of the cure. The demon of self-doubt is often the precursor demon to sickness, though. It is often a progression. Very few people latch on to sickness as their first demon to keep in their lives. This particular demon works in harmony with another demon. Alone, they don't seem to be able to keep hold of a person." Jason's mind was whirling with the idea of a tag-team set of demons attacking people, especially people that he knew. "Joe, do you think that you and John and I could have a cup of coffee this evening?" "Sure Jason, but I think I will stick with decaf. I don't want to caffeinate too late and end up awake most of the night." Joe chuckled a little after his comment and it made Jason smile as well. "What time would work for you and should I ask John, or would you want to do that?" Joe responded, "I am good about 7:30 and I can get John there. Let's meet at my usual café." "That sounds great Joe. I really appreciate you moving our meeting up and for getting John there." "It's my pleasure," said Joe.

With that, they said their goodbyes and headed out into their day. Jason really wished that he could take the day off altogether and head out to talk to them now. This was important and he didn't want to waste another day and he really didn't want Steven to waste another day. Jason had quite a bit on his to-do list for the day, but took several times during the day to simply open up and listen to his guide. He didn't know what he was listening for or whom he was listening to. He simply knew that he needed to listen.

He needed to be open to whatever lessons would come his way. At lunch, he sat outside, which wasn't really his normal plan for lunch, but he felt compelled to sit and watch.

He thought back to the verse in Matthew that he had learned when he was in Jr. High Sunday School. It was something like, "Look at the birds of the air; they do not sow or reap or store away in barns, yet the Father has provided for them. Are you not more valuable to the Father than they?" He watched the birds in the courtyard near his office. They were hopping around and pecking at the ground. They didn't seem unhappy at all. They had purpose to their activity and seemed to always find what they needed. Jason wondered aloud, yet really to himself, "I wonder what is so different about them that they know how to be happy each moment." As he said it, it hit him. They lived in each moment. They didn't live in the past of what has been wrong. They didn't live in the future of what might be wrong. They didn't worry about catching a cold when the winter came. They simply headed South to warmer weather. They hit each problem in their life as it arose and not before it arose. They lived fully in the present of their lives. How cool would that be, he thought. How cool would it be to live in the moment and not allow the past or the future to sway your happiness. How much better would we be if we did that?

Jason thought about how Steven was always talking about what the next steps were in his life. He never looked at good next steps, just bad ones. He thought the worst about himself, about his well-being, and about life itself. He seemed to live simply to embrace unhappiness and sickness. Jason wondered if that was the way that the demon of sickness worked too? What if people got sick in their mind before they got sick in their body? What if they compounded their illness by focusing just on the bad that might come, instead of living into the good that actually was in their life at the time?

At that moment, Jason noticed something that was a greyish black on the side of a person that was walking in the courtyard. As Jason noticed it, the thing looked back at him with both contempt and anger in its eyes. Jason thought that he should be scared, but he focused on the moment and simply took in the sight. He knew without being told that this was the demon of sickness. This was what he felt when he was around Steven. He had no idea how to get rid of it, but he had felt the same internal response every time he was around his friend. The man was hunching over a bit and looked somewhat pale. His physical body reflected his state. What was interesting to Jason, though, was the fact that the demon seemed to be pulling the man's upper body down and pushing in on his abdomen. The demon was pulling the man's body into a position of looking ill.

Jason remembered a study that he had read after attending a self-help seminar about looking happy versus looking sad. The study had concluded that when you make your body look happy, you tend to be happy. When you make your body look depressed or anything else, you tend to become the way your body looks. Was that the demon's job, he wondered. Was it his job to make the man's physical posture look sick and then the man could be more easily swayed to be sick? He thought about Steven and could clearly see an image of him, always looking sick. This demon wasn't alone, though. Jason looked up at the man's head and could see a demon that was a lighter grey, but seemed to look, well, like confusion. Every now and then, that demon up by the man's mind would make a motion toward the man's head and a red flash would happen in the man's mind. He seemed to be throwing bad thoughts at, no into the man's head.

Jason couldn't seem to stop watching the man and the two demons. He had never actually seen a demon before on his own and this was scary, amazing, and freaky all at the same time. He couldn't imagine what it must have been like for John to get this when he was young and not have anyone prepare him for what it would be like. The man continued to walk until he was out of the courtyard and Jason's attention shifted back to the birds and the lesson that they had for him. It didn't seem that they sat around worrying about anything. He was thinking that the Bible verse that he learned so long ago had meant just that. Don't sit around and worry. Live in the moment and live every day that you are alive. The verse never promised immortality to the bird. It never said that it wouldn't face hardship. Instead, it reminded us that the bird is provided for and is less of a treasure to God than a person is. It was the knowledge of our value as people that was embodied in the lesson along with the fact that we can choose to live in the present.

Jason went back to work and finished up his day, accomplishing quite a bit more than he thought he would. He organized his desk and got rid of a few things that he knew he would not deal with, and filed away the things that he was finished with as well. He felt a strange sense of peace about living in the moment that he really hadn't felt before. He was excited about seeing Joe and John. He would have just enough time to swing by his place and change to jeans, then head to the café. He would grab a sandwich from the house and eat it on the way out there so he could stay focused on the conversation and not on hunger. He caught himself starting to drift toward what was next and how to handle it, and then he pulled his mind back to the present moment. He pulled out his notebook and wrote.

I live fully in each moment of each day. I am here, in the present, and trusting that I am loved and that everything is good.

He shut the notebook, stuck it in his bag, and headed for his car. He changed quickly when he got to the house and made himself a sandwich and grabbed a bottle of water. He felt lighter, even healthier. He was living in the moment and deciding on things as they arose, without putting too much thought into them. He headed to the car and hit the AUX button on the stereo. The music from his phone began to play through the car stereo. He loved classical music and Beethoven was the last thing that he had listened to. It was on Scherzo Allegretto, which always made him pretend that he was conducting an orchestra for some reason. It had a good pace to it and it seemed to help him see the joy in his life. He listened to almost a dozen of Beethoven's best by the time he reached the café. He turned off the car just as a brilliant piano run ended. He was happy and he was in the moment as he went in.

"Hey Joe! Hey John! It is great to see both of you!" Jason spoke first and seemed to be happier than either of them had seen him before. In fact, he was happier. He was also more intrigued about his lessons than ever before. He couldn't wait to ask questions of the two, but especially of John. He jumped right in. "Ok John, I have some questions for you." John let a half smirk curl up on the left side of his mouth and said, "You saw one, didn't you?" "How did you know that I saw a demon?" "I knew that you saw one Jason because your spirit changed. I can tell that you are now a seer." Jason was as surprised that John knew as he was that he had actually seen the demon of sickness. Joe was also intrigued. In all of the years that he had been connecting people with each other, and especially with John, nobody else had seen a demon the way that John did.

Joe couldn't help himself. "What was it like, Jason?" "It was scary and cool and interesting and fascinating and heart-wrenching all at the same time. I wanted to go over to the guy tell him but I knew he would think that I was completely nuts if I did." "What did you end up doing," asked John. "I started to get scared when I first saw it. I was sitting in a little courtyard area and eating and thinking. It just all of a sudden appeared on the side of this guy. I instantly knew what it was because I had the same exact feeling when I looked at it as I did when I was with my friend Steven." John asked, "Does Steven bring on a lot of illnesses also?" "Yes he does. He seems to be able to read about something bad and then, BAM, it magically appears in his life." "What else did you notice," asked John. "Well, I noticed that it didn't seem to work alone. There was a second demon that I was able to notice as soon as I focused on just observing the demon of sickness. It seemed to be kind of cloudy, like it was confusing the guy." "Did it seem to be throwing ideas into the guy's head and was there a little red light or spark in his brain when that happened?" "YES! That is exactly what I saw." Jason was really getting excited now. It was like he had just been introduced to reality for the first time. Everything else that he had considered real somehow seemed to be less relevant.

John looked at Jason thoughtfully and proudly as he said, "Jason, welcome to my world! It is an amazing ride to be a seer. You can tell so much about a person and can really help them out when you are able to see what is actually going on in their lives. I want to try something with you right now." "Anything," said Jason. "I want you to close your eyes and see the scene all over again and then listen to what you hear about making the man's life better. Just listen to the guide that is inside of you. What are the steps that your guide is telling you?" Jason closed his eyes and thought about the scene in the park. He pictured not just the man, but everything that was around him. Strangely enough, he was able to circle the scene in his mind and see everything that was going on. He could see the front, back, and sides of the man and could see the demons from every angle. He felt as if he was actually all around the man. He slowed himself and began to listen to the voice inside of him. "This man needs to have a definite purpose in his life. He feels as if he is on his own and questions the reason for being alive. He isn't sure about the point of this world. You need to help him. Be his friend and listen to him. Ask him about his dreams and what he wanted to accomplish when he was younger. Do not feel sorry for him, but push him to take action. Definite action will refute the demon and give him something more powerful to focus on." Jason was hearing these words, almost as if someone was sitting right next to him and whispering in his ear. He wanted to open his eyes and see if someone was there, but he knew that it was a voice from within him. He kept listening. "Once the man has a purpose, a drive for his life, he will then need to develop his confidence. This is done through behavioral affirmation and the building of relationships. He has never been good at relationships because he has not known what to say or what to do in them. This weakened his will to fight off illness. He has used the illness to gain attention and give his life meaning. He doesn't even know that is what he is doing. Guide him to live with definiteness and confidence." Somehow, Jason knew that it was time to open his eyes, so he did. Joe and John were both sitting quietly, patiently, staring at him and waiting.

Joe spoke first, "Well, did you hear the guide?"

"Yes I did," said Jason proudly. "I heard exactly what that man needed. It was incredible to be that in-tune with everything." John said, "We are given what we need when we need it, Jason. Most people never take the time to listen, nor do they truly desire to help another person. When your heart is pure and your mind is quiet, you will hear your guide." Jason couldn't believe what had just happened. It was incredible. "Okay, Jason, I want to know what you have learned about the demon of sickness and how you are going to use that knowledge to help others," said Joe.

"Okay, the lessons that I have learned are…

1. This demon preys on people who are already weakened. In other words, it works with another demon to bring people down.
2. It's power is diminished, if not outright destroyed, when a person has a definite purpose. Despite the attacks on a person, it has little power to prevent them from their destiny if they keep their focus elsewhere.
3. It seems that people will invite this demon in when they feel they are knocked down, or when they are in need of attention, or when they don't know how to relate to other people in other ways. I don't want it to sound like anyone who is sick wanted to be. I can see that people are attacked against their will, but there are those who seem to ask for illness through this demon and outside of their conscious thought.

4. It takes a strong will to focus beyond this demon. One's inner guide holds the answers to how to overcome it, if the person will quiet their mind and focus on desiring good for others.
5. Finally, this demon, like the others, only has the amount of power that we allow it to have. In fact, this one feeds off of the work of the others in order to survive. Otherwise, it is sick all on its own and cannot do anything.

"That is impressive," said John. Jason smiled and took a sip of coffee. "Thanks, John. I am so excited by the lessons that I am learning. This knowledge is exciting and scary and cool and I have no doubt that it will change my life forever. This world that we live in isn't just the reality that most people accept. It truly is a world that we create through our thoughts and what we choose to accept in our lives. I have no doubt that I will be definite about my purpose from this point forward. I also plan to see if I can find that man again and help him to see the right future for himself." Joe looked at him. He was learning the lessons that he had hoped he would. Jason really was going to master this realm. Joe said, "Jason, I am proud of the choice that you have made to learn about the rest of the world, the other reality that many people ignore. This is going to serve you well in overcoming your fears. When you overcome them, you will accomplish every goal that you set for yourself. I have absolutely no doubt!"

The three men sipped their coffee quietly and thought about the lessons that Jason had learned. John thought back to what it was like as a kid to learn those same lessons. He had longed for a guide to help him make sense of it at the time. Now, he was proud to be able to help Jason make sense of his journey. Maybe that was the point of my struggles, he thought. Maybe he needed to struggle in order to know how to help others to get quickly through their learning curve. John was the one that finally broke the silence of thought after what must have been at least 10 minutes of contemplation and reflection.

"Jason, you are going to change this world. You are going to help people find their purpose and overcome their fears. You are going to make an incredible difference in people's lives, and for that, you will be blessed."

The three men toasted with their coffee and they simply knew it was time to head their separate ways. On the way out the door, Joe said, "Jason, you have one more lesson to learn. I would like to introduce you to my friend Lewis this Saturday. When you moved this meeting up, I knew it was for a reason. Within minutes of you changing things up, Lewis called and asked if we could meet this week instead of next." Jason's eyes widened. He was very excited about moving up his learning and amazed at the power of connection between all things. "We really are all connected, aren't we," asked Jason. "Yes we are!" said both John and Joe in unison. The three chuckled a little about speaking simultaneously and then headed off to their cars. Jason now knew about the demon of sickness and he wouldn't let it slow him down ever again.

6 AGE – OLD AGE & DEATH

Things were so different now. It was amazing how understanding and awareness could change the entire world around him. Jason could see so much more of the actual reality that existed. He could see who people really were and what really made them tick. He could see what was holding them back and what was dragging them all the way down. He thought back to a quote that he had heard when he was in his Introduction to Psychology class in college. William James, who was considered the father of American Psychology had said, "That which I perceive is my reality." This was so true. Reality was determined by perception and interpretation. He thought about the number of people who existed with a misaligned perception of reality. The wrong perception would keep a person from living the life that they could have had. The wrong perception could position them for failure and pain and misery instead of success. Jason closed his eyes and thought about how understanding had changed him and how it would continue to change him going forward. "I will strive to continue opening up my perception and understanding of the world as it really is." He said this out loud to nobody in particular. He just knew that it needed to be said. His life would never be the same. It would become ever expansive as he took in all that this understanding of what was really out there had to offer.

Jason took a walk to have time to think and reflect. There was a park near his home that had a walking trail around it. It was a beautiful area with lots of trees and birds and even some squirrels. The sounds of nature in concert with the gentle reassurance of a breeze and the warmth of the sun were inspiring. He was aware of his surroundings and at the same time able to escape the world of his thoughts. Jason was curious as to what the next demon would be that he would be exposed to? He wanted to expand his possibilities in life and needed to understand each of the threats in the other realm in order to do that. He concentrated on opening his awareness and removing his filters. As he did, he found it necessary to sit at the next park bench that he came to. He was seeing more than he had imagined was possible.

Jason looked at a woman that looked physically young from her external body. When he looked closer, he saw a different picture. He saw a decrepit woman that was ugly and miserable. The spiritual woman that appeared was one that was wrinkled and unhappy and full of self doubt. He thought back to the combination of demons that he had seen with the demon of criticism and self-doubt working on the person to create sickness as well. This demon seemed to be working in unison with both of the previous ones. There seemed to be the demon of criticism on the woman's back, the demon of sickness clawing at her, and this new demon integrating itself into her body the best that it could. Each time this new demon advanced, the woman seemed to try to pick up her pace a little. It was as if she was fighting against them and, at the same time, inviting them to stay. What was this thing, Jason wondered?

A new person came close to him, this was a person who was old in their physical body, but seemed to be clean from demons altogether. There was no self-doubt, no demon of sickness, and no ugliness integrated into their very being. As he focused on this person, he began to see a different perspective. There was a sort of light that emanated from the person. They were filled with, well, it looked like positive energy. They were emitting light from their being. It was cool. As Jason focused on this person, he felt himself feeling more positive and more energetic. He couldn't help but feel better as he observed, and somehow seemed to connect with, the person walking by him. Neither of them said anything, but they seemed to be aware of one another. The man was walking with his dog, who seemed to be just as happy as he was. What did he have? Was it just the absence of demons? It didn't seem like that. It seemed like he had something more.

Jason got up and continued his walk. He passed 4 more people, each with a different sense about them. One was beautiful on the inside. One was sad on the inside and full of self-doubt. Another was, well hollow on the inside. The fourth one was full of light, just like the other gentleman that had passed him. Each person seemed to have a unique spiritual signature about them. It was a unique combination of who they were from the inside out. Jason could see how they saw themselves. Their internal view seemed to influence the energy field around them. When they were down and near him, he began feeling negative. When they were positive and near him, he began feeling great. Their energy influenced his energy when he was open to them. He wondered if they were feeling energy from him. He really wanted to expand on this, but he had some work to do that morning. He headed back towards his house to go about his day. It would be time to visit with Joe again very soon. He concentrated on how

Joe helped him feel more positive about himself as he walked home. When he arrived at the house, Joe had left him a message on his home phone.

"Hey Jason. For some reason, I was just thinking about you this morning. When you popped into my head, I wanted to call and talk to you or leave you a message. I think that what you are learning will really change your perspective on life. You will start seeing things and feeling things that you didn't know were possible before. The next demon that you will learn about is the demon of old age and dying. This is one that has our country in its grips. You will know it because it integrates itself into a person's very being. It also works with self doubt and sickness. John has described this one to me and to the others that I have worked with. Be on the look out for it and focus on being a light to others. This is the easiest way to drive this one out of our lives. I look forward to seeing you on Saturday at our usual spot. John and I will be there to talk about what you have observed throughout the week. Be blessed, my friend."

"Ain't synchronicity cool?" Jason had to observe this out loud. He thought of Joe after observing a new demon and wondering what it was. He had seen the man emitting light and seemed to be absent of this demon. Then, Joe had called and left an answer for him. That's the way the spirit works, he thought. We truly do live in a friendly universe where the spirit wants us to have answers and grow and succeed. It only works if we listen, though. We have to be open to what the spirit has to offer us in order to receive those gifts of information and wisdom. Jason knew that he had spent most of his life being closed off to what existed in this realm that had always been there. He was so thankful to be a part of it now. He picked up the book of quotes that was on his end table and opened it up. It landed on quotes by Einstein. The first quote that he saw was, "I want to know the thoughts of God. The rest are details." Einstein was right! "I want to know the thoughts of God as well!" Jason said this out loud and then contemplated the meaning of what he had said. Understanding what was happening in the spirit made the rest of life seem like secondary details. He would devote his time to understanding that side of reality and how it influenced, or even controlled, the rest of reality. The physical realm seemed to be more a reflection of the spiritual realm than separate from it. People that had their spiritual life in order seemed to also have their physical life in order. Those that clung to demons as their truth seemed to have their light diminished, or even extinguished altogether. He would inspire light in others. He would live his life as a reflection of the light that existed and would inspire others to do the same.

Saturday can't come soon enough!

As Jason arrived at the café, Joe and John were already there waiting on him. He thought he was going to beat them because he was 25 minutes early. Jason smiled to himself as he got out of the car and headed in. By the time that he hit the door, the waitress was bringing him a cup of coffee. It arrived to the table as he was shaking hands with the two men waiting on him. Jason had spent some time preparing himself to be open to the spirit before he came to the meeting. He wanted to see what these two men really looked like. He was astonished at the amount of light that came from them. They both seemed to light the room up. When he shook hands with each one of them, he felt something different this time than he had felt before. He felt their positive energy magnify when they connected. It didn't seem to diminish at all. Instead, it seemed to grow in himself and in the other man. It was so cool! A big grin went across his face as he released hands with John. He had already shook hands with Joe. Life really was what we were able to perceive in it.

Jason took his seat and took his first sip of coffee.

There was something that was so soothing about that particular coffee. Jason knew that it wasn't really the coffee itself, though. It was the energy of the group, all focused on helping each other to become better. That energy came through in the coffee, in the café and most definitely in the interactions between the small group. The more open he had become to learning about the true side of reality, the more he could feel both the good and the bad in those around him. Today was going to be an incredible discussion. He could feel it and Joe and John seemed to feel it also. He was ready!

John started, "One of the most fascinating demons that I have observed is that of old age and death." Joe had already had this discussion a number of times, but he was still fascinated by the topic and was a great contributor. "John, why don't you go ahead and expand on that for Jason." Jason was almost vibrating with energy, though, and he couldn't help but jump in himself. "John, I know exactly what you mean. I was in the park earlier this week and saw this demon. I could adjust my focus from the physical presence of a person to their spiritual presence. I could see their spirit, or aura, or whatever it should be called and I could see their demons. I have been seeing the demons as you described them to me, but this was different. I could see whether or not they were filled with positive energy or negative energy. Those who were filled with negative energy appeared to be spiritually old and close to death. Those who were filled with positive energy seemed to be filled with light and hope and appeared to be spiritually young and vibrant. This really had nothing to do with their actual physical body, though.

John had a huge grin on his face because he knew that Jason already got it. He had learned about this demon the same way that John had learned about it. He had felt the difference in the person and seen the direction of their energy. It was amazing to see another person become a seer the same way that he was. "So Jason, what was the most surprising part of this revelation for you?" Jason thought for just a minute and then said, "It was the response that it evoked in me. I was blown away that a person who was spiritually very negative seemed to make me see that and even feel that they wanted others to be, well uglier than they were. It was like they were in a race to be young and everything that they did simply made them older. They seemed to fear death and not know what to expect, or something like that. How do you see it John?" John was still smiling when he answered, "I see it very similarly to the way you described, with a few differences. When I see that a person has that fear of old age and dying, I see that they seem to be searching for ways that others will see them as younger. The strange paradox is that whatever we focus on, we tend to get. People who are affected by this demon are not focused on being young. They are focused on not being old. The more a person focuses on not be old, the older their spirit seems to become, which will pull their body in that same direction. This leads people to all kinds of diets, age-defying creams, and plastic surgery. It is an attempt to convince themselves that they are not getting old and dying. They seem to think that death is the end of their existence altogether."

Joe chimed in now, "Death is the end of this physical body, but it is not the end. The way I see it, death is what we have been working toward. We shouldn't accelerate it, but the spirit knows when we have done all of the preparation we are going to or we need to, and that is when we transition. If we are truly made up of this energy field, then we go back to that from which we came." John jumped in, "A person who does not allow themselves to be controlled by demons and who lives the life that was intended has nothing at all to fear in death. In fact, they will have a peace about them, knowing that they are headed to the right place. It is the person who does not take control of their spirit and therefore their thoughts that has cause for fear. They don't have to go toward the fear, though. The fear came from them giving up that control of their spirit and their thoughts to the demons. When we live in fear, we live without faith."

Jason took a few sips of his coffee, which was lukewarm now instead of hot. He thought about the waitress coming over to warm it up by filling the top half with hot coffee. As he was about to take his third sip, she showed up. "Want a warm up, hun?" Jason smiled and said, "sure." He moved his cup over in front of the waitress and she topped it off with hot coffee. She did the same for Joe and John. He seemed to be connecting better and better with the spiritual realm around him. This not only affected him, it also affected the people that interacted with him. He regained his thoughts about the subject at hand. "Okay guys, here is what I think. I think that people are convinced that they will not be loved if they grow older. I believe that our society and most of the marketing that we see in this world would indicate that growing old is a bad thing. Because it is seen as a bad thing, people fear it. If it were not seen as a bad thing, people would not be so easy to convince that it was. I think that this demon plays off of the person's self-doubt, shows them that they could be sick and weak, and leads to them feeling that they could not possibly be loved if they are not physically perfect. I remember reading a book by Maxwell Maltz called Psycho-Cybernetics. Dr. Maltz was a plastic surgeon who was fascinated with why people did not seem to be able to see themselves as beautiful after he had just transformed them into the physical representation that they had wanted. He would augment, or change a person who was already beautiful, but they wouldn't be able to see it. On the other hand, he would take someone who had been in a crash and had been disfigured and fix the physical abnormality, putting them back to the way they were, and they would be perfectly fine. He believed that there was something else going on in their head that prevented them from seeing themselves as beautiful." Joe jumped in, "I read that book. It was a great book and it demonstrated the power of thought. I think that the spirit influences a person's thoughts. It is their thoughts that ultimately define them, but they are sparked by the spirit." Jason smirked and started in again, "I would agree. Through this journey, I have been able to see things that I never realized existed and it has really helped me to understand why people think the way that they do. I think that Dr. Maltz sensed that there was something more than was being represented by the physical person. He studied the way that people talked to themselves, which would be represented by the demon of self-doubt and criticism. He studied the way that they took care of themselves and the actions that they took. His conclusion was that arranging one's thoughts in a particular way would lead to them behaving in the right way, which would get them the right results. Think about that as we compare the demon of old age and dying. If a person lives their life to the fullest and does not fear death and dying, then they don't skip the parts of life that make them truly feel alive. I don't think it means that people should be stupid in the way that they do things, but I do think that it means that people should take the trips, try the hobbies, and live the entire time that they are alive."

Joe and John leaned back in their chairs in unison. They looked at each other and then looked at Jason and then back at each other again. Joe raised his cup of coffee to make a toast, "To living life the entire time our physical bodies are alive!" The other two men quickly grabbed their cups and clanked them together with Joe's cup. "Here, here," John and Jason said simultaneously. John then added, "Jason you have the secret to not being controlled by the demon of death and dying. The secret is to live your life fully, experiencing the joy and struggle and opportunity of every moment. The secret is to live in order to leave a legacy of adventure and experience. When you live like that, you light the path for other people. You live your life so that nobody could possibly think that you were holding back. You live completely. You live!"

That was the lesson, thought Jason. That was the lesson that I needed to know about. It was the lesson that would help to separate his life from the world that was afraid. He would not be afraid of living. He would not hold back. He would focus on living every moment of every day. He would push himself to try new things, experience the joy of every moment, and live with fervor. He knew that his physical body would some day die, but his spirit would live on forever. He knew that living life as if it would soon be over and skipping the good parts to try to make it last only one more day was wasting all of the moments in between. He would not waste any of those moments. He would seize every opportunity in every day. He would take the risks that made him feel alive and he would inspire others to live their lives in such a way that they would know that life was lived in each moment of each day. To beat the demon of old age and dying, one simply has to choose to live, to embrace who they are in every moment, to find the joy and exhilaration of life in their surroundings each moment of each day. That is exactly what he was going to do. He didn't just think it, he knew it!

The three men continued their discussion for another hour about the people that they knew and what their focus in life was. They talked about people who lived in every moment and appreciated every breath that they took without fear of it being their last. These were the people who changed the world. These were the people that inspired greatness. Each man had their own example of a hero who lived life to the fullest. Each example led to a discussion of how to embrace that level of action and enthusiasm for life. Jason wrapped up their meeting, knowing that Joe and John had other things to get done with, "If you know that you are living your life to the fullest, there is never a need for fear of old age and dying. You are progressing on the path of growth, experiencing each moment. That is how I will live!"

With that, the three of them put down their money for their coffee, each leaving a nice tip, and headed towards their cars. The knowledge of what is and what should be would shape Jason and would keep propelling the others. Once you know, you can't let it go. You have to choose between being controlled by the demon and taking control of your life and your spirit.

7 LOSS OF LOVE

Jason woke up at 3:37 AM in a cold sweat. He looked over at the clock while swiveling around to place his feet on the floor and to sit up on the side of the bed. He had just dreamed of her again. He was distraught over the fact that he had lost her, but the crazy thing was when he had lost her. He had lost her in high school. That was nearly 20 years ago. "Why can't I get her out of my head?!" He was talking to no one in particular, but he had to ask the question. As soon as he did, he heard a voice inside of his head say, "because she was the only one for you and there will never be another one like her." He wanted to cry but found himself getting angry at the same time. He had only dated her for six months. Why did she have so much control over him? She had ruined every relationship that he had with a woman since then. Somehow or another he would think of her and then start finding flaws in the girl that he was with.

Misty had moved on. She was married and had

several kids. It didn't seem like she had even given Jason a second thought. After all, they were just kids at the time. Her struggle was not with missing Jason, it was with feeling inadequate in her relationship with her husband. She couldn't understand why he was always so upset. He was always mad, always upset about the house, or money, or the way that the world was unfair. Jason had run into Misty a couple of years ago. When he did, she expressed her fear of losing Keith because she just couldn't figure out how to make him happy. Secretly, Jason wondered if this would be when he and Misty would get back together. He wanted her back and felt that he would never be able to be happy with anyone else. Misty indicated that she thought he might have been the one that she should have stayed with, but she didn't really feel that way. She just said that because she was always trying to say the things that people needed to hear in order to be happy. When they were together in high school, she always knew what to say and was always trying to keep him happy.

Too much of his life had been wasted on wondering if she was the one. "I want you out of my head!" said Jason. Something happened when he said that out loud and with force. All of a sudden, his mind was quiet. He didn't have her running through his mind. Was it possible that he could have controlled this from the beginning? Was it possible that it wasn't her that was in his mind? Was it possible that this could be, yet another demon? Jason let down his guard and he could feel that fear of never finding love and the regret of losing her coming back into his mind. He flexed his new-found spiritual muscles and ordered the demon of loss of love out of his mind. He thought back to the explanations of the demons that John had given him on the first day that they met.

"Nullus Amor! You are the one that is planting these thoughts in my head. Show yourself to me!" This was the most bold and determined that Jason ever remembered feeling. As soon as the words left his tongue, in front of him stood a figure unlike the others. She was elegant and good looking and very, very sad. She was the kind of figure that you would want and would feel sorry for at the same time. She appeared to feel lost herself. She appeared to embody what Jason felt like when he was thinking about Misty. In fact, she really resembled Misty when he looked closely at her. She embodied what she was telling him that he could never have. He found himself wondering if he should let her back into his head, allow her to… "Stop!" he said out loud and with such force that the demon moved backward from him. Her energy could only occupy the thoughts of loss that he would feel. She seemed to plant the idea that he would never find love and if he did, it would be unfulfilling.

"Nullus Amor, you are going to talk with me. You are going to explain yourself to me. You are going to speak!" Jason didn't even know if it was possible for her to speak, but the knowledge that he had gained with this new gift had given him a boldness that he couldn't explain. He looked directly at her and said, "Tell me how you work. Explain yourself to me!" Nullus Amor looked around for a way to escape. She seemed to be afraid of Jason now, something that fascinated him. She, a demon, was afraid of me. He could sense her thoughts, but wanted her to speak. "Speak!"

She did. She looked at him and tried to regain her own control as she said, "Jason, you deserve to be happy. You deserve Misty. Her marriage isn't going to work. You need to wait on her." Jason looked at her and said, "I did not tell you to give me advice. I told you to explain how you work to me." She seemed to wince at the thought of explaining herself, but she began to speak again. "I find something that was good at one time and keep that in the person's mind so that they will be incapable of seeing the good in front of them. I take existing relationships and I help the person to see the flaws in their partner. I make them believe that they are giving too much to that person and not getting enough from them. I pull memories from a person's mind and make them better than they actually were. My job is to get each person to realize that they are not happy and, at the same time, to fear that they will lose what they have. I make them see flaws in themselves and I amplify those flaws. I tell them that they don't deserve to be loved and get them to ask themselves how anyone could possibly love them."

Jason looked at Nullus Amor and said, "You are the most contradictory demon I have encountered so far. You tell people that they deserve to be loved by someone else but they don't deserve to be loved by the person that they are with. You tell them that they should be happy, but not with the person they are with. You convince people of the possibility of deep and true love and convince them that they will never have it. Your cruelty is almost unfathomable." As Jason described how awful she was, she seemed to smile for the first time. "You like destroying people's hearts, don't you?" Nullus Amor looked at Jason and with a wry smile on her face said, "I do what I was created to do." The smugness in her voice made Jason realize that he did not miss Misty. He didn't need some demon controlling his life. He didn't need to turn over control of his life, his heart, to some idiot that wanted only despair for humanity.

"You are going to tell me the truth! You are going to tell me how you work!" The demon looked at him and said, "Very well, let's begin." She sat down on nothing in particular, but appeared to be seated in a chair. "One of the most powerful persuaders in the kingdom is me. I make women get surgery on their bodies because I convince them that they cannot be loved if they don't look like they did when they got married. I make men buy expensive things and I convince them to cheat on their wives. I convince them that love is always somewhere else. For women, I convince them that love will always be somewhere else for their mates, unless they do a little more to make themselves appealing. I convince designers to create clothing lines that only a few people could really wear on their own. I work everywhere in the minds of people to convince them that they will never be enough." Jason put his hand up to motion for her to stop and said, "I want you to give me a specific, step-by-step process that you follow. I want to know your method that you use." She glared at him, but seemed to be unable to say no. "Very well, there are really three steps that I follow. Step 1, I convince people that love originates outside of them. I convince them that they need someone else or something else in their lives in order to feel loved. If they don't have that one thing that I know will be outside of their reach, then they will never feel loved. I work on people as young as I can, usually starting on people by Junior High School. I convince girls that their bodies are unacceptable and that they will never be able to be loved for who they are. Once I have the thought of inadequacy planted firmly in their minds, obviously with the help of Dubium, you know him as doubt and self-criticism, it is fairly easy to manipulate their thoughts. If love is always somewhere else, they will always feel that they have lost what they had or it will always be outside of their reach. What they don't know is that love originates inside of them. They will never be able to love fully or be loved fully until they love themselves fully. It is not until they love who they are that they can have the love of another person. I have created a barrier that keeps them from experiencing love until they accept and love themselves. Step 2 is to give them love. After I have planted the idea that they can never have what they want, I give it to them." Jason looked disgusted and confused and said, "Wait a minute. Are you telling me that you convince people that they don't deserve love and that they can never have it and then you give it to them?" "That's right. I give them the very thing that I have told them over and over again that they will never have. Once they begin embracing the idea that they have finally found what they wanted all along, I go to work on the third and final step. Step three is to destroy what they have. I do this by helping them see the faults in the other person, then convincing them that they are the problem themselves. I tell them that nobody could love them long-term. Now that the other person knows them, they will not want them. I start to harden their hearts so that the other person will start seeing their faults as well. I drive a wedge between couples. I make them spend more and more time apart and convince them that they are more unworthy and need to prove themselves further. This drives them to work harder, away from their mate, and then adds more guilt to their lives."

"You are the most cruel of any demon I have encountered," Jason blurted out. "Thank you!" Jason shook his head and said, "You go out of your way to destroy happiness at the most emotional level of any demon. I would imagine that people fear you more than death." Nullus Amor smiled again and said, "That's the idea. I steal their joy and often their life. I make them see that they are nothing without love and convince them that they will never have it. I destroy every aspect of their hope that I can." Jason said, "Now, I want to know how to beat you. I want to know how to get rid of you from a person's life." "I don't want to tell you that, but I don't have any choice in the matter. Telling you about this secret will destroy my hold on anyone's life that you share the secret with. This is who I am and what I was made for, don't make me tell you." Jason let a half smile come across his face as he said, "What's the matter? Are you afraid of losing the lost love of those you torment?" Jason could tell that this made her angry, but she did her best to keep her composure. "I simply know that you will be missing out on the memories of Misty if you do this." "Nice try, but I am already onto you. I want to know what to do to protect myself from you and to help countless others protect themselves. The secret that I have figured out is that you are powerless over those who claim control of their thoughts and you have to share with those who are seers. So, explain your weaknesses."

"Fine, but you probably won't know how to do this even after I tell you so you shouldn't really even try. There are only three things that a person has to do in order to beat me. The first thing that they must do is define what they are seeking in another person. If they get a definite image of what they are looking for in another, then those characteristics are drawn to them. It is not a specific person, but a specific image that matters the most. The second thing that they must do is to embody the things that they are seeking in another person. Like knows like when it comes to characteristics and values. You attract to you what and who you are. If you are a jerk, you will attract a jerk. If you are vulnerable and deeply in love, you will attract that. I will tell you that I do my best to plant the seeds of doubt in people's minds. If I can't convince one person, then I go to the other person in the relationship. That is why the third step to beating me is so important. Often times, people simply won't do this step and it becomes easy for me to win. The couple must be completely open with each other and must be other-centered. When they are continuously focused on the needs of the other person, I have trouble ever getting a foot-hold. When a person is self-centered, it is easy to get into to their head and manipulate them. When they are continuously focused on the other person, I find it almost impossible to even get a start with them. Being other-centered requires a self confidence that means Dubium, the demon of self-criticism and doubt, cannot have a foothold in their lives. They must be confident in who they are in order to be vulnerable in who they are with. This is simply choosing to take control of their own lives and to not let us in. Thankfully, very few people will ever do that."

Jason was astonished at the conversation that he had just had. Since meeting Joe and John, everything that he thought was real in his life was changed. His new perspective on how the unseen world of fear changes people's interpretations of reality was incredible. It was incredible and it was scary. He wondered how many times he had been subject to the influence of these demons. He knew that he had lost a lot of time and missed out on some great relationships because of this particular demon that sat in front of him. As he thought about all that he had missed, Nullus Amor began to smile a broad smile. For the first time, he realized that he had a choice about whether or not to give up the good in his current life for what might have been in his past. As this thought overpowered the thought of Misty and missing out on all those opportunities for love, the smile faded from Nullus Amor's face. She was definitely unhappy at the thought of Jason finding happiness. Jason looked directly at her and said, "I don't need you or want you anymore. I am choosing to focus on what I have and what I can have that is good. The past is the past and it is gone. My joy will not be determined by you or any other demon. My joy will be a conscious choice that I make. I will keep my focus on the present and will be grateful for all that I have in each moment. As he stated his new intention, he could tell that he really meant it. He watched as Nullus Amor faded away. She appeared to be scared as she lost her grip on his life. She would not longer take away what he had because of what he did not have. She was done.

Jason felt a peace about him over the next several days. He was alright. It wasn't that he was going to be alright at some point. He was finally alright in the moment. Everything around him seemed brighter again. The vivid colors that he had witnessed when he first began seeing the other world were even more intense now. Life was more intense. He had chosen to open himself to the possibilities that existed in front of him instead of hiding away in hopes that what had been would come back. He would find the person that would love him just for him, but he was in no hurry. When the time was right, they would appear.

Saturday morning finally came and it was time to head back to the café. This time, he would be meeting just with Joe. John had to be out of town. He was good with that. He was looking forward to the conversation. He was looking forward to telling Joe about what he had learned from the demon herself. As usual, when Jason arrived early, Joe was already seated and enjoying his coffee. He was going to make it his mission to beat Joe to the café next time. He wanted to be there first for once. He chuckled at himself for being competitive about drinking coffee first, but he knew it was a part of his makeup, and he was okay with it. He walked up to the table and greeted the waitress as she arrived with a fresh cup of coffee at the same time that he arrived at the table. "Good morning," he said. "Good morning Jason. It's good to see you again. You and old Joe have fun visiting." And with that, she turned and walked away, on to the next table.

Joe smirked a little before he uttered his first words. "You went deeper into the new reality, didn't you?" "How did you know that Joe?" "You look different. You look, well, relieved. I am guessing that you got some closure on lost love finally." "You knew which demon I would be meeting, didn't you Joe?" Jason was smirking now, thinking about Joe knowing what he was going to face. Jason leaned forward a little and asked, "Did you know that I had an actual conversation with her?" Now Joe sat up in his chair, "A conversation?" "That's right, I don't know exactly how I did it, but I got her to give me the steps to getting past her." Now Joe was intrigued. He had seen a number of people get past the demon of lost love, but he had never had a person engage in conversation with her. He had definitely never seen anyone pry the steps to beating her out of her. This was incredible. Joe put his coffee down and reached for his notepad. He looked at Jason and asked, "Do you mind if I take notes?" "Not at all; in fact, I am flattered that you would want to." Joe said, "Now, I want to know exactly what she said. She is a tough one and there are lots of people that will be better off if they can figure out how to beat her." Jason sat back in his chair a little and smiled. He looked at Joe and said, "So the student becomes the teacher." He kind of drew the statement out, savoring the idea that he actually had something to share with Joe that he didn't already know.

Jason took a sip of his coffee and started in on the formula that he had learned from the demon. "Okay, here it is…

1. Define what you are seeking in another person. You have to have a clear picture of what it is that you want in the relationship. Whether that is respect or fitness or whatever, you have to have a very clear image in your mind.
2. Embody the characteristics that you want from the other person. Like knows like. In order to have something and attract it into your life, you have to be those things. People are drawn to people with the same values and characteristics as they have when the person is definite about what they want.
3. Be other-centered. She says that this is the most difficult one for most people. I think that is because our society is so focused on the self. You don't hear about people taking 'otheries.' You just hear about them taking selfies."

Jason was actually a little surprised at how simple the formula sounded. He knew that most people didn't and probably wouldn't follow it, but it really was pretty easy to beat this demon. Joe said, "One thing that is interesting is that she didn't say that there was only one person for each of us to love. Instead, she said to focus on the characteristics and image of the type of person you want along with living as a representative of those very characteristics." "You're right Joe. She didn't say that we have a soul-mate for real. What she said, when I was talking with her, was that she uses the idea of a soul-mate lost in order to steal the happiness of people." Now Joe was thinking about the times in his life that he had experienced those pains of not knowing in relationships. Jason continued, "Knowing the three steps that have to be followed to beat this demon really gives me the perspective that the demons of fear are only as powerful as we make them. When the formula is easy, all the demon has is the illusion of control. In reality, we are in control when we choose to take control." "That's right Jason. It is just like the other demons. You had to have a definite aim, be the right person, and focus on helping others. When you do those three things, it seems like you can beat most of these demons without all the struggle."

"I know that I don't want to struggle when I don't have to. In fact, Joe, I would rather be successful and happy and not stressed out any day over struggling to make things happen." "Me too," said Joe. With that, the two of them continued their conversation about Nullus Amor and what she looked like to Jason, what she sounded like, and what it felt like to interact directly with her. Joe was fascinated by every aspect of the story. He had always wanted to be a seer, but had never been given that gift. Some people were meant to see and some were meant to coach, thought Joe to himself. They talked for another hour about that experience as well as the other experiences that were leading up to the conclusion of their journey together. Jason knew that there were six demons that they were discussing and he knew that this was number 5. He knew that the last one was Anger, or Iratus. He wasn't sure what the sessions after the last demon would be, but he knew he wanted to find a way to stay connected with these guys. He had already learned so much and he knew that his life would never be the same. As he would soon find out, this last demon was going to be a tough one.

8 ANGER – IRATUS

"Jason, I can't believe that you would allow others to treat you the way that you do. You should be outraged at them. You deserve better and they deserve nothing good for what they have done. Any rational person would be upset right now. You have good reason to be angry. They have cheated you. They are talking bad about you. They are trying to make you look stupid. That salesman that you talked to yesterday, he was a jerk to you! Nobody should ever try to close you like that. You should say something to the company. You should have him fired."

Jason woke from his fitful dream. He had been sitting at his kitchen table when a man sat down across from him and started telling him about all of the things that he should take offense at. He woke up feeling angry at the world. He wanted to punch someone, but he didn't really know why. As he tried to relax and refocus, he thought about the last conversation that he had with Joe, just two days earlier. All of a sudden, he heard that same man's voice in his head saying, "Joe doesn't care about you. He does this because you will pay him out your profits. What has he really even done to help? He talked to you about imaginary creatures! Wooo!" "Stop it," Jason said aloud and with quite a bit of force. He went back to the conversation and thought about the fact that the last demon that he would learn about was the demon of Anger. When he finally pieced it together, Jason said aloud, "Nice try! I know that you are there Iratus. Show yourself. We need to talk."

With that, Jason smiled and headed towards his kitchen to make himself a cup of coffee. Although nothing happened right away, Jason just felt as if he would meet his next foe some time that day. He would be watching out for this demon and be ready for his next attack. He knew that he had already experienced one of them in his dreams and another when he drifted back to his last conversation with Joe. This guy might be tough, but he was confident that there was a formula for beating him as well. Jason went about his morning, taking his shower and getting dressed. Just to be sure that he was ready, he dressed to impress. He would be headed out to talk with a guy he had known for some time about a business idea. It wasn't Jason's idea, but Alan almost always had great ideas. He didn't always execute those ideas well, but the guy was always thinking. He worked hard in sales and ran across a lot of interesting folks in his travels. Even if his idea was mediocre, Alan was sure to have some great stories about his adventures.

They were meeting at 10 AM at a local coffee shop in the downtown area. This would be different than the café experiences that he was now used to with Joe and the others. Alan was a mover and a shaker and made sure to meet where he knew that he would run into influencers. This was definitely the place for that. Those type of people were always in this downtown shop. Jason got there 15 minutes early and Alan got there about 3 minutes before the meeting time. Jason already had his coffee when Alan got there. As he came in, he waved to Jason and then shook hands with several others that he knew and probably wanted to know a little better. After he got his latte, he joined Jason at the corner table.

"Jason, man it's good to see you. What have you been up to? How is the transition coming? Have you picked what you want to do next?" Alan had a habit of firing off several questions without taking a breath, a habit which irritated most people. It usually didn't bother Jason, but he seemed to be a little agitated by it this time. Jason took a deep slow breath and broadened a smile across his face. He looked at Alan and said, "I'm good. I have been learning a lot about life and about success and about what holds us back. I haven't decided exactly what I am going to do next, but I know that I will not be afraid of whatever it is."

Alan pulled his head back a bit and tilted it to the right. He had a puzzled look on his face by Jason's answer. "Something not make sense, Alan?" Now Alan began to smile and said, "I just had a conversation with my wife this morning about how fear has kept me from trying several of my ideas." He paused for a moment as if trying to figure out exactly how to say the rest of what he was thinking and then he continued. "Actually, I would say that fear has kept me from trying any of my ideas, and I have a lot of ideas." Jason said, "So, do you think that you would be doing something else if you weren't afraid of the outcomes?" Alan shook his head a little while seeming to stare off into space. He was likely picturing what it is that he would be doing if he wasn't afraid. "I would definitely do something different if I had no fear of failure." Jason gave Alan a knowing look, as if saying that he could relate and understand.

Alan's look shifted from definite to anxious to angry. He seemed to be really upset about something. Jason asked, "OK, you seem to be shifting thoughts. What are you upset about?" "Well, I am just thinking about all of the things that I thought of before anyone else was doing them and then somebody else did my idea before I did. It makes me so angry at them for somehow stealing my ideas, even though I don't know them. I get even angrier at myself, though, for not acting on the ideas before everyone else does. I get angry at my wife for not pushing me to pursue them. Then, I get angry at myself for being angry at her because it isn't her fault." Alan stopped and took a drink of his latte. Jason said, "It seems like you are angry regardless of the direction that your thoughts take. You are angry at yourself, other people, and then at yourself again. Why do you think that you haven't acted on more of your ideas?"

"Jason, that is the $64,000 question. I really wish that I knew why I hadn't taken action on more of the ideas that I have had. Heck, I wish I knew why I haven't taken action on a single idea that I have had." Right as he said his last statement, Jason noticed another man beside Alan. He didn't look like a demon, though. He just looked like another man and he looked really irritated. He looked angry. He leaned over and whispered in Alan's ear. As he did, Alan blurted out, "I am furious at the fact that I have a gift of coming up with great ideas and no follow through." "Why do you think that is?" The man leaned toward Alan and whispered in his ear. Alan then said, "I just don't have what it takes to run my own show, I guess." As he said that, the demon of criticism and self-doubt peeked around Alan's shoulder and began darting negative thoughts into his head.

Jason was fascinated by this process. This demon didn't appear to be a demon at all. He appeared to be a well dressed man, that seemed to be, well, logical looking. He was able to act before criticism and doubt. Once the demon of self doubt showed up, the man seemed to get a smirk on his face. As he was watching this unfold, another person walked right through the man. It wasn't around him, it was through him. He was plain as day to Jason, but obviously wasn't seen by the others in the coffee shop. Jason looked at Alan and asked him, "Are you successful at your current job?" Alan looked directly at Jason instead of looking off in the distance and said, "I am very good at my job. I hold all kinds of sales records at the company. I make great money and they love me there." "So, have you proven that you know how to bring in business if you are focused on it?" Alan had an almost cocky smirk on his face when he said, "I can bring in business better than, well, anyone that I know!" He kind of drew out the last four words of the sentence as he said them. Jason then asked, "So, knowing that you have consistently proven that you can bring in business, and knowing that your company loves you, what part of a product launch intimidates you?" Alan didn't want to come across as scared, but he had come across exactly like that. "I hate thinking that I am intimidated by anything, but the truth is that I am unsure if people would want to buy something that was my idea. I'm not really that worried about whether or not I could figure out how to make a product or provide a service. I have been involved enough in this company to know that I could do that. I'm just not sure that people would want it if it was my idea." Jason said, "Let me ask you something. If you took one of your great ideas and tried to sell it to yourself, would you buy it?"

Alan looked a little puzzled, but after only a short hesitation, he said, "Of course I would. I would buy it all day long." "So, Alan, what you are saying is that you know you could make your first sale in the first minute that you were in business. Is that correct?" Now Alan was chuckling a little. "Yes. That is exactly what I am saying." "Great, you have done the first thing that you have to do in order to overcome your fear. You have bought into your ideas.' Alan said, "Just like that?" "That's right. It is just like that. Let it sink in Alan. The only thing that you are missing is the order in which you make your first sale. You are trying to get someone else to buy into your idea before you do. If you buy into it, I don't think that there would be any stopping you." The demon beside Alan leaned over and whispered in his ear again, but before Alan could say anything, Jason continued. "Don't get mad at yourself or at anyone else right now Alan. Right now, you just have to decide if you really buy your idea that you and I are about to talk about. If you do, decide to be happy about the brilliant idea that you have had. In fact, be happy that you are blessed with incredible ideas regularly." "Whoa Jason, how did you know that I was starting to get mad?" "I have developed a gift of being able to tell a few things about people and their fears. Let's just say, you were about to lean in to the idea of being upset." Alan started to smile at Jason and the demon that was seated beside Alan got up and walked away. When he did, the demon of criticism and self doubt simply vanished. He no longer had the attention of Alan to feed off of.

The two of them began talking about Alan's idea. It was a great conversation. In fact, Alan's idea was so good that it would solve several of the problems that Jason knew had been keeping a number of his executive friends up at night. They talked for the next two hours about how Alan's system for mapping problems would work and how it could be turned into a web application that anyone could use. It wasn't just a project management application, like so many of the others that Jason had seen. It was a logic map that would make it easy to see the possibilities of each action. It was better decision making, wrapped in logical processing, wrapped in project management, and delivered with strategic thought and contingency planning as its foundations. It was awesome! It was something that Jason was really interested in being a part of. And, it was a reflection of the success patterns that Alan had demonstrated!

"Alan, you are facing much of the same challenge that others face. In fact, your demons are not unique to just you." "My what?" Alan wasn't sure what this was all about, but he was intrigued. He had heard his father talk multiple times about conquering demons, but that was the only person he had ever heard talk about them. Alan asked, "What do you mean by demons?" "Well, I mean that you have these things in your life that hold you back. They keep you from accomplishing the things that you were always intended to accomplish. With you, I see that you get angry at others and then you shift the anger to yourself. Once you do that, you begin questioning whether or not you even have the ability to do what you want to do. Once the criticism and self-doubt creep in, you get more angry at yourself and then you doubt yourself more. It is like a vicious cycle of negative self-fulfilling prophecies." Alan was speechless because he knew that Jason was right. He could see that cycle in himself. He knew that he did get mad externally, then internally, then he doubted, and then he got even angrier. He hated it, but he didn't know how to beat it. "Okay Jason, if you can see it, do you know how I get past it?"

As Alan asked the question, the answer was clear in his mind on how to overcome the demon of anger.

"There are four steps that you will need to follow. I will warn you, though Alan, these will require you to make a definite decision about who you will be from this point forward. I need to know that you are willing to step into the life that is better and that was always intended for you. Are you ready for that?"
"Am I ready? Am I ready? Absolutely! I am ready to be the best version of myself that I can be! Let's do this!" Alan put his hand up in the high-five motion and Jason slapped his hand hard. When he did, several people in the coffee shop turned to see what they were so excited about. Jason raised his hand and mouthed "sorry" to those that were looking on. Several people laughed and one guy even gave him a thumbs up. Jason turned to Alan and said, "I guess people really do like seeing a little enthusiasm." They both chuckled a little and then Alan raised his eyebrows as if to say, I am ready for that answer now.

"Okay, the four steps that you will have to follow are…

1. Surround yourself with the right people. When you have people around you that believe in you and support you and encourage you to be the best version of you possible, then you will have the right mindset for success.
2. Don't blame others, including yourself. Instead, just accept your part in the choices that were made. Once you accept your part, you will know what to do differently.
3. Make a plan of action to make things

better and then work the plan. If you keep focused on what you need to do to make things better, then things will keep getting better.

4. The last one might seem a little crazy, but it really does work. You have to look happy. This requires some discipline because you won't always feel like making yourself look happy. Smile and hold yourself like a happy person would hold themselves. If you start to feel the pull of anger, change your physiology and that demon loses its hold on you.

Alan said, "Well, those weren't exactly the things that I was thinking you were going to say, but that sounds doable enough." Jason leaned back slightly, feeling satisfied with the wisdom that had come to him. He knew that it wasn't directly from him, but was from somewhere else and just came through him. "Alan, you have great ideas. You are great at business, and I would love to figure out how to work with you on this idea, even if you just meet with me and we brainstorm on how to make it happen. There really are things that attack people's thoughts. In order to be successful in this life, you will have to learn to battle and defeat your demons. This can sound scary to some people, especially those that have never had a lot of luck with winning that battle. It can be done, though, and you can do it. You just have to follow the steps." Alan replied, "I can do that, but my dad used to talk about battling his demons. He used to say that each man has his demons and he must defeat them in order to create the life that they desired." Alan paused and Jason jumped in, "and you are wondering if you father meant figuratively or literally?" "Well, yes and no. I think each person has to make their own decision about what that represents. What I am wondering is, what are the demons that people have to battle? It's just that it seems like you are pretty in tune with this area. My dad talked about them as things that he was afraid of and had to beat. Is it something like that?" "I would say it is precisely that, Alan. Each person has to face their fears and overcome them in order to live a life of freedom and success. Your dad was a smart man." "Yes he was. I admire him and want to live life without fear like he did, as much as I can anyway."

Alan looked down at his watch and grimaced a little. "Oh man, I gotta run. I am late for my next meeting. Jason, I can't thank you enough. I literally feel like I am not carrying around another person anymore. It's like I am down to the one self that matters the most." Jason smiled because he knew that the statement was actually true. "Have a great day Alan! Let's get back together soon!" Alan responded, "Absolutely brother" and then stood up and headed out the door.

Jason thought about all that had just happened and knew that he had to come up with an easy to apply formula to beat these 6 demons of fear. This would be his quest. He would listen to the wisdom that was out there and create a simple formula to follow that would allow anyone to overcome the 6 demons of fear. All they would have to do would be apply the formula in the right way and they would be free. Just like he had witnessed with Alan, this freedom could instantly change the way a person saw the world. He was built for this. He would live into his purpose by making this formula easy, but incredibly effective.

For the next four days, this was Jason's focus with any bit of extra time that he had. He wanted to get as much of it ready as he could before his meeting with Joe on Saturday. He needed to get Joe's input. After all, Joe had been working on this for some time. Surely the two of them could come up with the right plan and make this happen.

By the end of the week, Jason had about 10 pages of notes in his journal. He had gone through all of the lessons that he had learned on this journey. He was looking for the themes on how to overcome these demons. Once he had the theme, he could put together the steps. Then, he would be able to teach others how to face and beat their demons and enjoy the lives that they were designed for. He didn't want to get ahead of himself, but he simply couldn't wait for the next lesson before he started developing the secret formula.

The 'secret sauce' is going to make so many lives better, thought Jason. It will have the power to transform anyone that applies it in their life. He said out loud, "Man, I get goose bumps every time I think about being able to make a lasting impact on a person's life. I just can't wait to see Joe and run all of this past him." Jason had even labeled the top of his notes pages as 'Secret Sauce For Defeating Demons.' He listed out each of the demons, what their weaknesses seemed to be and what had worked in defeating them. He listed out what they were strong in and what the human weaknesses were that seemed to make people subject to their control. He also listed out all of the reasons that he could think of that people willingly give up control of their own lives to each of the demons. This would be the work that Joe and him could do on Saturday, and Saturday couldn't get there soon enough.

9 SECRET SAUCE

Jason got to the café almost an hour early. This was the very first time that he had gotten there before Joe. He wanted to make sure the he went back through all of his notes before they met. He wanted to be sure that the information made sense to him and that it would make sense to Joe as well. This was a very big day and he wanted it to go off without a hitch.

As he sat down and began sipping his coffee, he pulled out his notebook and looked over the notes that he had made during the previous week…

Each of the demons that we face is there because we have allowed them to be in our life one way or another. Each of them needs us a lot more than we need them. When a demon attaches itself to a person, it usually starts with the person experiencing self-doubt. People doubt the abilities and gifts that are inside of them and then start to talk down to themselves. When they do this, it opens the door to attacks. The end game of the demons as they attack seems to be that they want to push people to anger at others and then finally anger at themselves. Once a person turns their anger inwards, it comes out as depression. There is a formula for beating each of the demons that attacks us.

The demon of criticism and self-doubt, known as "Dubium," tries to get people to see the things that they do wrong instead of the things that they do right. In order to beat this demon, one must have a definite purpose in their life. When a person has a definite purpose, the roadblocks diminish. Second, one must believe in their ability to learn. Self-doubt is the worst when a person believes that they cannot learn.

For the demon of poverty, known as "Paupertas," his objective is to get people to focus on their fear of poverty and to put as much attention as possible on being in poverty. This demon passes from one generation to the next. He continuously gets people to compare themselves to others that are better off financially than them. To beat this demon, people must measure their worth in their relationships and must live in gratitude for all that they have. It can't matter how much that is. It is the attitude of gratitude, instead of the fear of poverty, that leads to this demon losing its power.

The third demon is the demon of sickness, known as "Aegritudinem." This demon slows people down by getting them to focus on what is going wrong in their body and works in conjunction with self-doubt. This demon is defeated when people shift their focus to a definite and chief aim in life and realize that their physical body, physical pain, etc., are only temporary. When a person lives a life of purpose and passion, they move beyond the restrictions of their physical pain. It takes waking up every single day with a focus on your mission in life in order to get past the pain. When people work in jobs that are not inspiring or do things just for money and not for their passion, they focus more on their physical limitations. This demon tells people that they will only get attention if they are sick. It tells them that people will love them if they are hurting, but not if they focus on moving forward. Self-belief, focus on a chief aim, and positive self-talk make it possible for people to get past this demon. People have to have something bigger than themselves to focus on.

The fourth demon is old age and death, known as "Antiquis Mortem." This demon tells people that there is an age that they reach that makes it impossible for them to succeed, grow and learn, or move forward at all. It tells men that they need a younger woman and material things in order to matter. It tells women that they will not be wanted or valued if they look or act their age. It strives to create a fear of mortality, often working through the churches to compound the fear. Often times, this demon will attack church-goers by telling them that they have not and cannot do enough to make it to heaven. It gets them to focus on striving to be a religious person in order to avoid the fiery pits of hell. To beat this demon, it takes a strong focus on establishing your belief about life and death and the afterlife. When people make their worth based on the external opinions of others, they are very susceptible to this demon. When a person operates their life out of fear, instead of a drive for their purpose in life, they are a prime target for this demon. This demon often works in conjunction with the first demon, just like the demon of sickness does. Having a set of daily objectives, or a daily method of operation, will open a person up to succeed in overcoming this demon.

The fifth demon is probably the most powerful of all of the demons. She is the demon of lost love, or "Nullus Amor." This demon convinces people that they will have nothing of value in life because that are not, or cannot be loved. She tells people that they cannot live without a certain person that is unavailable to them. She destroys relationships by driving people apart, using other people. Sometimes she uses children. Sometimes she uses old relationships. Sometimes she uses work. She is ruthless and only cares about convincing people that they cannot and will not be loved. In order to beat her, one must operate with gratitude every single day and in every single moment. They must live in the moment and not in the future or the past. It is the moment, and only the present moment, that holds the truth of the blessings that we possess. She is defeated only when a person focuses on the things that they have and how grateful they are for those things and those people. One must have a clear image of what they desire in a relationship. They must embody those characteristics, since like attracts like, and they must be other-centered and not self-centered.

The sixth of the primary demons of fear is that of anger, also known as "Iratus." This demon operates by convincing people that the only way to protect themselves from pain is to insulate themselves with anger at others. People will give up relationships, riot, attack others, and focus on all of the bad in the world in order to be the one that struck first. This demon gives people the illusion of self-preservation while actually destroying their happiness. It convinces people to hate others that it can convince them are oppressors. The truth that defeats this demon is that people are only oppressed by their fears which are created by the demons of fear. Joy is the counter for Anger. When people do the things that help them see joy in the world, including focusing on the fact that they have control over themselves, then Iratus cannot maintain control. As a nation, this demon has had an incredible control over people. It incites people to hate people of another color, or who are different. Iratus creates a fear of others and then convinces people that others want to oppress them. We must see people as people instead of as a label in order to overcome this demon. Operating with joy and unconditional respect will position us to be victorious.

Jason read back over all of his notes and looked for the common themes for the demons. He was looking for what would make it possible for others to succeed in overcoming them instead of being controlled and destroyed by them.

Joe walked in, about 25 minutes before they were actually supposed to meet. Jason looked up in the middle of his thought and let a big smile curl up on his lips. Jason stood to greet Joe as he walked up. "Well, well, well, look who decided to be super early today." Jason smiled even bigger at Joe's comment. Jason said, "Well, I wanted to make sure that I gathered my thoughts beforehand. I wanted this meeting to be extra productive." Jason and Joe sat down and the waitress appeared almost out of thin air. She had a cup of coffee in her hand for Joe and a pot to refill Jason's coffee. The two of them exchanged pleasantries about the week and the weather for a few minutes as Joe got his first cup of coffee down.

Joe shifted the conversation. "It looks like you have had some breakthroughs this week. You sounded very excited on the phone when we spoke and you look like a kid on Christmas morning right now." Jason blushed a little and said, "I guess you could say that I had some breakthroughs alright. In fact, I think I have figured some of these demons out.

I am excited to talk through what I have learned about them. I think I am beginning to see a pattern in how you overcome them, but I wanted your opinion." Joe noticed the paper in front of Jason and asked if those were his notes. Jason told him that they were and pushed them over in front of Joe. Joe asked, "Can I read them and think through them for a minute?" "Sure," said Jason.

Joe spent the next 10 minutes just reading and re-reading the notes that Jason had put together. He was looking at Jason's description of each demon and what he thought would allow people to get past the demons. He was noticing the same pattern that he was sure Jason had noticed. Each demon gets their power from creating fear in the mind of the person that they are attacking. Without the fear, there was no power. The fear seemed to always come from the mind of the individual and not from reality. This was the lesson that Joe had been teaching people for years. It wasn't reality that scared people. Instead, it was the fear that people injected into reality. It was the fear of what could go wrong, or the fear of what was wrong, or the fear of the unknown. The demons had power only when people stopped focusing on their purpose in life or when people had not established purpose in life. Joe finally looked up at Jason and said, "This is very interesting. I see a theme in what you have said. It looks like a person has to do only about three things to overcome all of the demons. Do you see the three things?" Jason looked at him and smiled. "I see a few things, but I am not sure that they are the same as you. What is it that you see?" Now Joe smiled and said, "You first."

"Okay, Joe, what I see is the following three actions that a person must take in order to overcome each of the demons of fear.

1. A person has to have a definite purpose for their life. When a person is drifting, the demons are in control. When a person is focused on a specific end result, then the person is in control. This means that a person has to have a purpose regardless of where they have started.
2. A person has to quit waiting for someone outside of them to bring them success. Success comes from action, not from inaction. We are supposed to have a definite purpose that is fueled by forward movement at all times. When the demons can convince people that they are being held back by someone else and they can convince people of a lack of control, then they win. Action is based on positive self-belief.
3. A person has to fill their life with good stuff and not bad stuff. What we read, and watch on TV, and look at on social media, all have an impact on us. It is like putting bad gas into a car when we put bad things into our minds. When a person puts bad gas in, their engine breaks down. In order to maintain a smooth running mind, we have to have the best fuel possible. Everything that we put into our minds has to be there to build us up. So many people watch shows and movies that teach them to be upset and to not trust others and to live a life of drama instead of a life that

they are in control of.
At least, that's what I see." Joe looked at Jason and let a very satisfied and impressed look form on his face. Then, he added, "I think you are right on with those three things Jason. Whether we live in fear or live in victory is really based on purpose, action, and reinforcement. I might have worded it a little differently than you, but I would not have changed the intent of the message one bit."

Jason and Joe continued the conversation about those three fundamentals. The amazing part for Jason was really the fact that it wasn't a 20 page formula for defeating these demons. It was something that was very simple to articulate, yet still provided its challenges in the implementation. "Joe, how do you understand your true purpose in life? This one has given me trouble. In fact, that was one of the original reasons that I needed your help." "It isn't as complicated as one might think, Jason. In fact, it isn't discovering your purpose that a person does." Jason said, "Okay, I'll bite. If we aren't supposed to discover our purpose, what are we supposed to do with purpose?" "The simple reality is that you are supposed to define your purpose. It isn't a discovery as much as it is a definition. Some people will have a grand purpose for 5 years, others for 50 years. Your purpose can change if you decide to change the definition. Having a purpose that you define and embrace is what matters Jason. You have to define your purpose. There isn't a lightning bolt delivery system. It is you allowing yourself to try things and then simply deciding on the direction for your life." Jason looked a little concerned still and said, "But what if I start down a road and then realize it is the wrong path?" "What do you think you could do Jason?" "I could just change direction."

Joe looked across the table at Jason and said, "I think you are starting to understand that you really are in control of yourself and your direction. I think you are finally getting that it isn't something external to yourself, but rather it is something that is inside of you that sets your course. You have always had the power inside of you. God is a part of who you are. He isn't something out in the clouds somewhere watching to see what happens. He is inside of you, giving you the power that you need in order to fight the battles that you are in the middle of. If you are waiting for Him to show up, then you are ignoring the fact that he is the spark that is you. He is you. When God spoke to Moses and Moses asked whom he was to say had sent him, God responded with telling Moses that God is the 'I am' of the world. One of the fundamental reasons that people fail in this world is that they believe that God is only in church or off in the sky somewhere. When they claim God in every fiber of their being, then they know that they have the power to defeat any demon. They know that they have the power to love others even when they are not experiencing love in return."

Jason sat quietly for a few minutes, just digesting what Joe had said. He knew that they were dealing in the spiritual realm, but he had not really put it all together. He had always thought of God as this being in the sky that looked down on people and either approved of them or disapproved of them, kind of like Santa Claus keeping a list of who was naughty and who was nice. The idea that God lived inside of everything was a game changer for him. Jason finally broke his silent thoughts by asking, "So, if God is a part of everything, how are there demons and what is their purpose?" "That's an excellent question Jason. A demon isn't the opposite of God. It is the absence of God. Demons are here to try to get people to turn from creation. Their job is to be the 'anti-matter' of the world. God intends for you to live a happy, full, and successful life. He intends for you to be happy because He is a part of everything that exists. To turn your back on God is to turn your back on creation itself. What is the opposite of creation, Jason?" "That would be destruction." Joe said, "That's right. Destruction is the un-creation of what was meant to be. Just like cold is the absence of heat and dark is the absence of light. It is only when we turn from the power of God, the power that is us, it is only then that the demons have control."

This was a lot for anyone to digest. Jason was very glad that he had absorbed the information first-hand through experience. He wasn't sure if he would believe the idea of demons unless he had seen what they were doing in his life as well as in the lives of others. He knew that not everybody was a seer. The gift of seeing the demons had made it significantly easier for him to understand their plans for people. Now that he understood what they were and how they operated, he didn't want to find himself under their control any more. In fact, he didn't want to see other people under their control. As that thought went through his mind, he knew what he would choose as his purpose moving forward. He knew how he would make the world a better place and defeat the attacks on his own life from the demons of fear.

Jason knew that it would be his purpose to live as an example of success. He would wake every day with a grateful heart, a focused mind, and mission to accomplish. He would fill his mind and his life with positive things and would look for the good in everyone around him. He would no longer allow others to define who he was or whether he was happy. He would take control of his mind and his heart. By doing so, he would be able to pull people in the right direction. He would share these lessons with as many people as he could. He would work with entrepreneurs to help them create something great in this world by living without fear. For the first time, Jason knew, not thought, knew that his life was going to be one of significance and success.

10 AUTHOR'S NOTE

This has been an interesting journey for me. This is the 11th book that I have written in one year. It has been, by far, the most challenging, but not for a lack of creativity. It has been challenging because of the experiences that I have had in my life and in my family as I wrote about each of the demons. I found myself under attack by each of the demons as I exposed them for who and what they are. When I wrote about the demon of criticism and self-doubt, I questioned my abilities more than I can remember doing so in a very long time. The formula in that chapter is what I had to tell myself in order to beat the demon. I lived the challenges that I described in the chapters. When the demon of sickness was being exposed, every person in my family got sick. That never happens! When I wrote about the demon of old age and death, I lost two relatives to death. When I wrote about the demon of anger, my daughter was angrier than I have ever seen her, and she is a teenage girl. (Insert sarcastic expression here.)

Each of us faces challenges in our life. The greatest challenge that I see in the world right now is a lack of purpose, though. I have seen people with chronic illnesses, who usually find ways to avoid the world, light up when they find their purpose. The lie that we have believed is that our purpose is to make money. Our purpose is to define our purpose and live into that. I believe that when we are creating and making the world better, we are living into our purpose. This is done by designing houses, writing books, creating art, doing accounting, cleaning house, raising kids, loving our spouse, by being who we are and not who someone else thinks we should be.

The great challenge is to not buy into the lie of marketing and society. In fact, I think that we have been deceived over and over again into believing that we, being who we are, are not enough. Popular media says that the world is bad and that being yourself isn't enough. Truth changes things. Truth reveals that you are an expression of the Creator. Truth reveals that life is about choosing a path that creates something beautiful for the world and makes the world a better place. Deception and fear push people to destroy, control, and take away. I want to live in truth, even if there is a struggle involved. Because the truth is that there is beauty even in the struggle.

So, I will close out this book by encouraging you to choose your path. Choose your destiny and then fill your mind with positive stuff. Avoid the news. Avoid the negative. Avoid the commercialism that tells you that you aren't enough. Embrace the truth that God is in every fiber of your being. Fill your mind with truth and joy. Choose to live a joyful life. Choose to bring joy to others and to build them up. When you do, you too will defeat the six demons of fear and live a life of victory!

To Your Success!

Jody N Holland

ABOUT THE AUTHOR

Jody Holland is an author, speaker, trainer, and entrepreneur. He has written 12 other books, before this one, and spends time every week expressing himself through writing, coaching, speaking, and training both online and in-person. Jody has faced fears most of his life and began a personal quest at the age of 10 to overcome the things that were holding him back from succeeding. He strives to challenge others to push themselves beyond their fears and roadblocks and to live in the present, as the best version of themselves.

Made in the USA
Middletown, DE
14 October 2021

50256999R00075